C000145674

SCOTT AND SID

Written by ALI WRIGHT

Based on the screenplay 'SCOTT AND SID'
by SCOTT ELLIOTT and SID SADOWSKYJ

First published in Great Britain in 2017 by

Dreamchasers Film Ltd
© Dreamchasers Film Ltd, a UK Company

"Scott and Sid" adapted for the screen by
Scott Elliott, Steve Nesbit and Sid Sadowskyj

A CIP catalogue record for this book is available
from the British Library

I S B N (HARD BACK) 978 1 9998841 0 9
I S B N (E- BOOK) 978 1 9998841 1 6

10 9 8 7 6 5 4 3 2 1

Typeset by Dreamchasers Film Ltd
Designed by Scott Elliott and Sid Sadowskyj
Cover image © 2017 Dreamchasers Film Ltd

Printed and bound in Great Britain by Clays Ltd, St Ives plc

"We are what we believe we are"

- C.S. LEWIS

INTRODUCTION

by Author ALI WRIGHT

Scott and Sid are the kind of characters a novelist dreams about. They arrived in my life fully-formed. Walking and talking, downing whisky, already alive off the page, charismatic and sometimes awkward raconteurs with a stellar story to tell. They are best friends. They are Yorkshire-born and proud. They are film-makers. But above all, they are *Dreamchasers*.

Back in 2001, as teenagers growing up on different sides of the tracks, Scott Elliott and Sid Sadowskyj sat down in Scott's book-strewn bedroom and raged against the injustices of a world that equated intelligence with academia, happiness with money and fear with cowardice. They decided to tackle the problem head-on, arguing long into the night on the small-print and finally putting pen to paper to write their code for living. They called themselves *Dreamchasers*. By identifying a list of ambitions leading to an ultimate dream (to make a film before they were thirty), they set in motion the incredible series of events that was to transform their lives away from the humdrum stasis they grew up in. Their definition of what it means to be a Dreamchaser hasn't altered since its first incarnation. Scott and Sid have the original document to prove it:

A Dreamchaser is an individual with the courage to follow their heart and the belief to succeed in the path that they take.

Ultimate freedom comes from the ability to follow the one thing you want the most in life and the audacity to overcome the fears that lie in its path.

Without influence and pure in thought, a Dreamchaser is free in spirit, has a ferocious passion for living and shapes their own destiny.

Every generation has its defining cultural movements. A way of positioning yourself at the helm of your own life, steering your own course through uncertain times alongside like-minded souls. Think of any Twentieth Century movement and you are immediately drawn to those fearless, often involuntary, ambassadors who may not be at ease in the spotlight but shine nonetheless. The Dreamchasers movement is the perfect fit for our world. In an era where we can access knowledge any-time-any-place, with a seemingly endless plurality in how we can define ourselves, our values and our choices, there has never been a greater time to take a close look at our dreams. History is punctuated with people who make things happen, who storm forward ahead of an idea and drag it into being, while the rest of us stand on the sidelines. The feature length film depicting the story of Scott and Sid's life together - their visual manifesto - is the realisation of an ultimate aim scrawled at a kitchen table when they were teenagers.

True to that ambition, the cameras started rolling on their film-set the year Scott and Sid turned thirty.

It is almost impossible to speak of them separately. Scott and Sid are always together and they hold each other in high regard. They talk with the easy laughter of two people content in each other's company, the space between them laden with in-jokes and enthusiasm. One of the advantages of writing about real people is not having to guess their habits and nuances. The task carries with it a daunting responsibility, since personalities are kaleidoscopic and nobody quite views himself or herself in the way that an outsider does. As it turned out, Scott and Sid were benevolent subjects, happily opening the door on their quirks and vulnerabilities to help craft authentic characters, a kind of hologram version of themselves in ink, while allowing the author enough creative license to ad-lib on their back-story. The resulting novel weaves fact, anecdote and fiction through its pages, while the spine of the story – the idealism of Dreamchasing – remains true to life.

The novel is peppered with references to cultural icons from the Dalai Lama to Shakespeare, from motivational speakers to countless films, but the boys treat each quote and experience with equal gravitas. Eleanor Roosevelt's adage that "you must do the one thing you think you cannot do", that you should feel the fear and do it anyway, is frequently taken to extremes in their story, and it is this openness to emotional experience which really forms the crux of what it means to be a Dreamchaser. It is, as Scott says in the novel, "all experience, every second of life, you just have to tune into the details." With their heads in the clouds and their feet on the ground, Scott and Sid bound from one dream to the next, learning from their mistakes and allowing their sense of humour to prevail. As Scott implies in the last line of the film, there is no turning back.

Dreamchasing as an ideology rolls quickly off the tongues of the real Scott and Sid. They are adept at letting their own imaginations take flight and documenting the common ground that they discover. Part of the appeal of Dreamchasing is its holistic nature. It levels the playing field, embracing everyone and learning from everything. Scott and Sid are committed to the applied act of chasing their dreams and this means, firstly, not discounting a thing.

The Dreamchasing mindset manifests in the way that Scott, with his relentless optimism and boundless energy, has grown to look on the bright side of insomnia, his Moleskin notebook always at hand to document inspiration. In their shared home, any available canvas - their fridge door, whiteboard, shower tiles, every scrap of paper - is covered in red marker pen, no surface safe from Scott's thoughts. Sid's calm exterior belies a steely determination and an unrivalled work ethic. His persistence is something that could never have been in doubt for the most recent person to invest in the Dreamchasers project, who registered 27 missed calls from Sadowskyj before finally picking up the phone out of sheer frustration. The executive reiterated an absolute lack of interest in the film, telling Sid "I'm 99.9% sure it's not for me." Sid's response? "But that means there's a 0.1% chance you are interested, and that's good enough for me!" Sid stayed up the whole night to research the potential investor. When it came to meeting face-to-face the following morning, Sid's pitch was personal and irrefutable. The executive was won over. Signed up there and then.

At Dreamchasers HQ, there is no such thing as a typical day since, as you will discover, neither Elliott nor Sadowskyj do things by half. Where others would hand over the reins of a project for an easy life, Scott and Sid will always be found at the heart of anything upon which they embark: painstakingly editing each word of this novel, writing and re-writing the dialogue of the film-script to check it rang true, personally interviewing each potential film intern to ensure they shared their vision. Such tenacity means that they have in production not only the film and this novel, but also have developed an App which lifts the veil on film making, detailing the process from script to screen. They eat, sleep and breathe their projects. It's a metaphor that appears time and again in the novel, this Dreamchasing life-blood coursing through their veins. Their all-or-nothing ethos holds centre stage on the page, taking the shape of ultimatums and blazing rows as the fictionalised versions of themselves navigate the distance from dream to reality. In real-life, they are entirely sincere. When Scott says he is "jetting off to London", he means just that: that he is about to board a Citation X private jet headed for the capital.

Scott and Sid's charm lies in their ability to elevate you from the ordinary and make you believe in magic. They are rapidly inspiring a splinter group of adventurers. They possess just the right amount of ego, confident enough to know that their story is important, but humble enough to always see the best in those around them. They are always looking to give others a break, to pass on the baton in the perpetual dream-chasing relay.

Asked which living person he most admired, Sid answered, without hesitation: *"That's easy. Scott. I spend more time with Scott than any other person. He never stops trying to better himself and the people around him. He recognises his weaknesses and always seeks a solution to better them and grow. He chooses to fight and never give up... His courage, honour, loyalty and energy. He is the only person I measure myself on."*

Scott was equally inspiring when asked what advice he would give to his sixteen-year-old self: *"Dream higher. Do more. Don't listen to them. Help others."*

A recurring image throughout an early draft of the novel was Scott's nightmare in which he sees himself withering away as an old man in a nursing home, forgotten and uninspired. It is Scott's determination not to let that happen - to never allow himself to succumb to an ordinary path through life - which has motivated him from a young age. The story is not plain sailing. In the characters' journey through teenage life, extremes of emotion, social exclusion, family drama, tales of long-spun-and-not-quite-requited love and, above all, the unwavering bond between Scott and Sid, we recognise ourselves. It gives us courage for our own lives.

It is easy to be enthusiastic about the Dreamchasers project because, ultimately, it is a tale about friendship. It is about embracing life and everything it throws at you, and emerging on the other side a little stronger, a little wiser about yourself and your place in the world. While they are not typical heroes, there is something valiant and humbling about Scott and Sid's willingness to bare their triumphs and misfortunes. On the page, on the screen and in person, Scott and Sid will make you believe that normality is over-rated. Become a Dreamchaser and celebrate the weird, the wonderful and the uncertain. Chase down the 0.1%. Make curiosity your way of life. Embrace adventure on your own terms.

CHAPTER 1

Scott lifts his red plastic sunglasses to read the black ink scrawls on the back of his hand, as he contemplates the question. It's a habit he can't shake: in the spare moments between real life and dreams, Scott Elliott, aged fifteen and a certified outsider, hears voices. Today it's an interviewer, Los Angeles drawl and airbrushed smile, a far cry from the grey school yard where he's actually standing. Scott visualises himself in the third person: aged thirty, on the set of his own film, sitting in the director's chair with his Ray Bans on, taking it all in his stride. He closes his eyes tightly for a second. In his mind, the interviewer is asking about the turning point, about the day that changed everything. When Scott opens his eyes, the voice has been silenced. He's back in the playground, and the school bell is clanging. He takes a pink bouncy ball from his pocket, slams it hard against the tarmac and catches it without looking. Same shit, different day. He looks again at the back of his hand, struggling to read his own writing. He turns his head a full one-eighty. The head honcho's name is "Olsen", their appointment time 8:45am. Right on time. He assesses the building in front of him. Blackfriars High is the same uninspiring construction of red bricks, blocked drains and unwashed windows as every other inner city comprehensive school he's set foot in. Scott's beginning to lose count. He tucks his sunglasses into the top pocket of his creased white shirt, tugs at the hem of his vintage military coat and sets off across the yard.

It's over halfway through the school year, and the battle lines drawn on the first day of term are non-negotiable now. Scott knows without looking. There are the usual tribes, spread territorially across the tarmac like urban frogspawn: the first-years, still clinging to their friends from junior school and swapping football cards at play time; the popular girls who smell like Charlie body spray and bubblegum lip gloss; the awkward kids too chicken-shit to realise they'll never fit in anywhere, too scared to go it alone. Scott takes a final bite of his apple, tosses the core into a bin, wipes his hand clean on the burgundy jumper tied around his waist and weaves his way through the hordes. He'd known he was different the day he was handed over to foster parents. Why stop now?

Before the bell rings, there's an eerie haze to the empty classroom on the third floor. Light filters lazily through the dust and the scraping of the chair echoes around the room. A tall tree taps intermittently against the closed windows. The squawks and yelps of the people in the playground below fade into insignificance. Sid hooks his flimsy black gym bag over his favourite chair on the back row. He folds his blazer jacket over the back of the seat, trying to ignore the faint waft of cigarette smoke that clings to his uniform despite his best efforts. He settles himself carefully against the hard-backed chair and peels the top sheet from his value-brand notepad. Once the corner edges of the paper are perfectly aligned against the desk, Sid begins to write:

21st April 2001
Dear Sir,

Some mornings she's fine. I hear her downstairs, up even before me, and I lie there waiting for my alarm to go off, praying that this is the day she'll decide to go sober. She always hums the same song, and it haunts me for the rest of the day because I know that her good mood won't last forever. Especially not today. Today is the anniversary of the day nanna was buried. You were long gone by then. It's the day that gets to mum the most. More than the day nanna actually died, though there were howls and screams and swearing blind and a fit of rage that made our little house shake on that day too. But the day of the funeral, that's when everything really changed. I was too young to have a right to remember the details like I do. A broken umbrella that didn't stop the rain or my mum's tears making puddles in the soil. I was only five. But I remember it perfectly. It was the beginning of the vodka years. And there's no romance in it. It's filth. And it's been our life for the past ten years, since my mum watched her mum being lowered into the ground. Sometimes I wonder if it would have been different if you'd still been around. My nanna would still have got ill, her cancer would have come, would have spread, but you would have held my mum close and got drunk together, or not, and you would have been able to mend her in a way that I couldn't and everything would have been OK.

Sid keeps one eye on the door as he writes. It's funny how, at home, the words never come. Even though he has almost nothing and nobody to distract him. After eight o'clock, once he's put his mum to bed, he has no obligations, but whenever he sits in his bed with the paper on his knees and tries to write, the page stays blank. Here at school, in that non-time before the day officially begins, he feels like he has the space to be honest. He pushes his thick-rimmed glasses up the bridge of his nose and continues.

I try not to let her follow me to school. Today it's impossible. The significance of the day has latched itself onto my heels like a long shadow. I can practically smell the alcohol on her breath. I wish I could do what everybody else does. Stay at home when I feel like this. Be looked after.

He checks his watch, a candy-striped, Velcro-strapped Timex that he's had for eight years and washes once a week. Like his grandad used to say, pride costs nothing. He picks up his biro.

She'll be back in bed now, her second glass already half empty. I could run home, check on her, be back in time for Physics, say I had the dentist or something.

Sid stands up abruptly, trying to figure out the right thing to do. Often, he feels as though his whole world is dependent on a series of tiny decisions throughout the day, and he can never work out the right choice to make. His life has been woven around him without his consent, and he makes his steps faint so as not to make tremors in the fragile web that supports him. The only way Sid can navigate the web is to retrace his steps every day, and this manifests itself in a series of orchestrated neuroses: habits, routines and choices that get him through to the next day, like a computer game player stuck on level one. He latches open the classroom window, half an inch, just enough to peer out without drawing attention to himself. As if he knows anything about computer games, he thinks. Resting his chin on his jumper Sid notices a new hole in the wool. He folds the cuff up once more to hide it. It's nearly time for registration. Soon the hordes will be on the stairs, stampeding up towards him, filling the classroom with gossip and the smell of Lynx. He's never fathomed it out. How people find it so easy to make friends. How the hell you're meant to know who you can trust amongst the swarm. Five years at this school and he still hasn't a clue.

He tugs at a branch below the pane and a sycamore leaf falls to the ground like a helicopter landing in the jungle. Sid's attention is drawn to a lone boy making a beeline for the main entrance. The boy is tall and he walks head down, hands shoved deep into the pockets of his trousers. There's something off-kilter about the way he moves. It isn't a swagger, but the boy seems more sure of himself than most people their age. His blonde hair is messy and wet despite the dry day. Instinctively, Sid pulls out his nanna's old comb from his top pocket and runs it through his own dark hair as he watches. The stranger walks purposefully, as though he wants to get it over and done with, as though he has more important places to be. He's almost directly below the window now and Sid watches the boy so intently that he notices the double crown on his head, a kind of serpentine swirl, as well as the way his satchel is battered leather, the original strap replaced with an equally worn red belt. The sycamore leaf has landed in the boy's path, and, as he nears the window, he stops to pick it up. He pockets it. Then, without warning, he looks up.

The boy's cobalt eyes pierce Sid's for a second, and Sid bobs down out of sight. Great, he thinks. Another enemy to avoid. When he looks again, the boy has gone. Sid gently closes the window, makes a series of sharp folds in the letter he was writing and buries it deep at the bottom of his bag. He takes his seat and waits.

Here we go again, thinks Scott, drumming his fingers along the corridor walls and checking the brass plaques on the office doors. When he finds Olsen's headquarters, Scott pulls a stripy tie from his pocket, slings it around his neck and knocks.

Sid keeps his head down as his classmates settle around him. An arm knocks against his bag and Sid winces at the clink of the empty glass bottle hidden in there. He knows what people call him. Some names he can shirk off: Four Eyes, Dweeb, Polski. It's the ones that are closer to the bone that really get him. *Alkie.* Remembering the stings, he shrugs to no one in particular. Why shouldn't they call him names. It's not like he ever defends himself. God, he thinks, trying to wipe a smudge of ink from his clear pencil case and making it worse. I should have gone home. He taps out some quick sums on his calculator. Tuesday morning and he's already having to be creative with the benefits cheque. He'd hoped he'd have enough for some shower gel this week. Nothing fancy. Just something to make his mum smile in the morning. Remind her that he cares.

Standing at the front of the class, Scott wonders how many more times he's going to have to do this. He makes his face neutral and unreadable, refusing to give anyone any ammunition, not on the first day. He'd spent ten minutes in Olsen's office, listening politely as the headmaster assured him, with an air of misplaced superiority that made Scott feel uncomfortable, that this school was different to the rest. Scott waits for the class to stop talking and notice him.

Sid jolts instinctively and drops his calculator at the sound of Nigel Ball's voice booming from the back of the room. The class bully has an opinion on everything. Since he was old enough to realise the power of fear, Nigel has fine-tuned a specific tone that never fails to unnerve Sid in a fundamental way.

"Who's the pretty boy?" Nigel sneers, and the whole class laughs, predictably, skittishly.

Sid follows Nigel's voice to the front of the classroom. He recognises the boy straight away. Broad shouldered and scruffy, towering a foot above their form teacher, Mrs Finn, he demonstrates none of the timidity usually associated with new kids. This guy isn't looking to please anyone. His uniform is creased to hell, his collar already skewed at nine in the morning and his tie a token gesture Sid can't believe he's got away with. Sid recognises the piercing blue eyes from the playground earlier, but he sees now that there is no aggression behind them, just a sort of determined wild dreaminess that sets the boy apart. No wonder there's a pair of sunglasses in his top pocket. The boy has the kind of uncompromising stare that's asking for trouble in a place like this. Sid can't help but smile.

"This is your new classmate, Scott Elliott." Mrs Finn looks around at the teenagers. She dusts an imaginary speck of lint from her floor length floral skirt. "I trust you'll make him feel welcome. It's not easy joining a new school so..." Her voice trails off as she ushers Scott towards the room of hostile faces. "Well, take a seat," she urges. "It's not all about you, we've mocks to prepare for."

Scott hoists his satchel onto his shoulder and assesses his options before trudging towards a free seat, the frayed hems of his trousers catching under the soles of his tan Timberland boots as he walks. It's only one term, he reminds himself. You can keep a low profile for one term.

At the front of the class, Mrs Finn draws a few bullet points on the board and begins her preamble to the session on Steinbeck. Sid's fingers flit nervously against the spine of his second-hand copy of 'Of Mice and Men'.

As he is settling into the chair, Scott feels something warm and synthetic on the back of his neck.

"You're blocking my view, pretty boy," sneers Nigel.

Scott doesn't turn around. Instead, he peels the neon yellow chewing gum from where Nigel has stuck it just above his collar and, nonchalant and silent, sticks it to the bottom of his chair before standing up. He tries not to show his repulsion.

Mrs Finn tuts loudly and waits for Scott to settle down. She'd been warned about this one. He's come to them from St Jude's, the kind of school every teacher is glad to have dodged, the kind of school with metal detectors in the foyer. Mrs Finn clears her throat. She has no time for trouble-makers.

A moment of panic, as Scott scans the room again. He can feel the scarlet rising through his body, the rare seething anger beginning to uncoil and for a second he considers bolting for the door. Finally, he notices the boy on the back row, a slim, unassuming student wearing glasses. Sid nods him over.

"Thank you," mutters Scott under his breath as he sits down next to Sid and pulls a chewed pen from his satchel. He looks at his classmate. Scott's first thought is that the kid looks like a poster boy for a Work Hard Escape Poverty campaign. His second thought is pure gratitude. He rests his head on his palms and waits for his dreams to chase into the classroom and give him somewhere else to be.

The way he said it. Sid takes a bite from his sandwich. It tastes of nothing, orange cheese and butterless white bread, purely functional. He writes in neat, straight lines despite the plain paper.

Thank you, as though it was a big deal. Not thanks or ta or even he could've just said nothing. As though I'd made a difference. It was the first class in months where I didn't think about home. Scott, his name is. He had this weird habit of chewing the end of his pen and flicking the bits of plastic off the edge of the desk. It was kinda rank, actually. A couple of times, he hit me with the bits and I pretended not to be bothered. When he practically ran out the door at the end of the lesson, I noticed two things. One, that he had written a Shakespeare quote on the wood. And two, that he had left his pen behind. It made me feel sick to look at it, so I grabbed a tissue from Mrs Finn's desk, wrapped up the spit-covered pen and chucked it away. The quote though, that was the thing that really got me. He just sat there, tracing over and over the words, for an hour, and the quote was this and I wish I still had film in that old Polaroid you left in the house, so I could take a picture of it. Worst writing I have ever seen. He writes like a toddler. Did you know that you left your camera? It's a decent camera, I hope you don't mind me using it. I don't know if you know Shakespeare. Of course you know Shakespeare, you left a library of books behind. Anyway, the quote was from Twelfth Night, and it was this: Be not afraid of greatness. Some are born great, some achieve greatness, and others have greatness thrust upon them. And the thing is, Scott didn't even have a copy of the book and he wrote out the quote from memory. It was pretty weird.

Sid unscrews the lid of his ancient Thermos flask and takes a gulp of over-diluted blackcurrant juice. It tastes of plastic. Whatever, he's used to it. The jolt of the classroom door opening makes him jump, and he spills a couple of drops of the pale purple water on his shirt sleeve. He looks up, annoyed.

Scott is leaning against the door frame, scratching at his temple. He is out of breath, the sleeves of his shirt rolled up to his elbows, a splodge of what looks like ketchup on his shirt. The backs of his hands are covered in writing and ornate spiral drawings. "Did I leave my pen in here?" he asks.

Sid can hear the music blasting from Scott's headphones. Not your usual pop songs. Whatever Scott's listening to is all bass and cellos, the sort of classical music that film scores are made of. Before Sid can reply, Scott bounds over and begins to rummage around the desks, upending chairs, getting right down on his knees to look. Sid keeps quiet, suddenly feeling bad. Maybe the pen had a special significance. Like Sid and his camera. Like Sid and his anything.

Scott stops suddenly, defeated. "What you doing up here, anyway?" He flashes Sid a questioning glance. "You on detention or something?"

Sid laughs at the thought and shuffles a little in his seat. "Nah, it's just." He gestures towards the noisy playground below. "It's just quieter up here."

Scott stares at Sid for a second longer. "I get ya," he says. He suddenly remembers his music and presses stop on his mp3 player. It's true, he gets it. This lad needs his peace and quiet, just like Scott needs a constant soundtrack. When he's listening to music, he's not questioning where he should be, what he should be doing, whether there's a goddamn point to any of it. When he's listening to music, it's just him and the beat and the blood in his veins. He looks at the objects neatly arranged on the boy's desk, taking in the faded cartoon characters on Sid's plastic lunchbox. No wonder he eats alone. "What's the food like in this place anyway?"

"I wouldn't know," replies Sid.

"What you writing?" asks Scott. It doesn't look like school work and he wonders what could be worth staying indoors for on a day like today. The back of Scott's neck is still red from sitting out in the sun for the first half of lunch. He can't wait for summer. Walks on the moors and hitch-hiking to the coast. Being home before dark can mean eleven if he's lucky.

Sid suddenly remembers the letter and Scott's name in it, and he folds the page quickly out of sight. For the first time, he notices the giant eye drawn in black marker pen on the back of Scott's jacket. The piercing scrutiny makes him want to run for the door but something roots him to his seat, stops him from bolting.

Scott knows better than to push it. A thousand pupils in this school, and this kid is the only one who draws his interest. Scott doesn't believe in coincidence. He knows there's a reason they've met, the first friendly interaction with a peer in as long as Scott can remember, and he can't help but feel respect for this boy, with his old-fashioned clothes and unmistakable pride. He walks over to the window and opens it, considering the best way to get Sid on board. The fresh air is needed. The boy's clothes might be spotless, but they stink of cigarettes. "No matter how many schools I go to," says Scott in a confessional tone, "they're all the same."

"Really." Sid scoffs the last of his sandwich and packs his lunchbox quickly away. "How many you been to?" He ducks his head as a pink bouncy ball ricochets off the wall behind him.

"This is my fifth. Yorkie or Smarties?"

Sid looks at him blankly, until Scott brandishes a chocolate bar and a tube from his satchel. He rattles the tube in Sid's face and grins, showing pointy dog-teeth.

"Can I have the Smarties? Thanks." Sid awkwardly catches the tube, out of practice at team sports. Concentrating on popping open the lid, he tries to hide his astonishment. No one has ever been this kind to him. He eats in silence, thinking how much better it tastes than the cheap stuff, not knowing how to react.

"So, what's your story?" asks Scott through a mouthful of chocolate.

"What do you mean?" Sid has allowed himself to slouch in the chair, feeling relaxed for the first time in months but he stiffens slightly at the question.

Scott notices. He makes his tone casual, not intrusive. "I just mean, what you into?"

Sid begins to pack his flask into his bag, preparing for flight. He swallows the chocolate too quickly. Fuck's sake. He knew it was too good to be true.

"Do you like movies? Music?"

Sid looks at Scott cautiously. "Yeah, a bit. Don't get chance to go to the cinema much through." He stands up and secures his bag on his shoulders.

"Wait." Scott glances at the fresh scribbles on the back of his hand. "Can you show me where the library is? I wanna get some films out and apparently, I absolutely matter-of-life-and-death *must* register before two. What's the deal with Olsen, by the way? Ex-military or something?" Scott makes his back rigid and does a perfect impression of the headmaster's voice. He pitches it somewhere between Marlon Brando in 'Apocalypse Now' and Al Pacino in 'Scent of A Woman'. Times like this, he's glad for the cast of characters he carries around in his head. It's a relief when Sid finally breaks into a smile.

"Yeah," says Sid, laughing. "They're pretty strict about things around here. Sure, I'll show you the library."

"Can I borrow a pen, too?"

"Erm, yeah." Sid coughs nervously. "Sure. I'm Sid, by the way." He thrusts out his hand for Scott to shake. "Sid Sadowskyj."

Scott holds the door open for his new friend. "You've got to do something great with a name like that," he says, slamming his palm against Sid's back and bounding along the corridor after him.

They barely pass a soul on the way to the library, and Scott clocks that the route involves fire escapes, unpainted corridors and even a service lift. Scott comes to the conclusion that Sid is used to making himself invisible. He's the perfect tour guide: one loner passing on his hard-earned knowledge and survival mechanisms to another. Scott tries to show his gratitude by offering Sid first dibs on the copy of 'The Godfather Trilogy' that he withdraws from the library.

"It's alright, thanks, our DVD player's broken," lies Sid, quickly.

Scott notices the kind look that the librarian gives Sid, and he wonders how much time the kid spends in there. He wonders, too, if it annoys Sid, getting looked at like that, a kind of pity usually reserved for stray puppies and young widows. Scott couldn't handle that. He'd want to scream at the person, tell them he was just fine, he didn't need their pity thanks all the same. Sid, on the other hand, seems oblivious.

"You could have the locker next to mine," suggests Sid tentatively. Most of the other lockers are pasted in stickers. Sid's, top left, is pristine, except for a fist-shaped dent at head-height. Sid takes out a small bunch of keys and unlatches his padlock. There is nothing superfluous on the inside, either. No photos of bands ripped from 'Melody Maker', no sweet wrappers or muddy footballs. Just a neat stack of second-hand text books and an old pair of black canvas plimsolls. He swaps his copy of 'Of Mice and Men' for a heavy chemistry book with the cover missing.

Scott opens his satchel and throws a few random possessions into the locker next to Sid's. A gadget that looks like a games console. A spare pair of expensive-looking headphones. Some brand-new

Nike Air trainers with the price sticker still on the soles. A litre bottle of Lucozade and a bag of apples. He throws in the library DVD of 'The Godfather Trilogy', rummages in his bag for his padlock and slams the locker door closed.

Sid watches him with his book clutched to his chest, aware of the time. He has to make it over to the science block before the bell rings. But Scott is still talking and Sid isn't ready to say goodbye just yet. It's been good not to spend the whole of lunchtime alone. Not that he minds going solo usually, but it's that thing they say, there's no going back once you've tasted freedom. He's reluctant to use the word friendship yet. But it's been fun to have a wing man, even if it was just for half an hour. He shakes the tube of Smarties at Scott in offering.

Bang!

A hand comes out of nowhere and smacks Sid in the back of the head, pushing him against the locker, and the metal slams his face, cold and unforgiving. An ugly splat of chocolate smears over his mouth and chin. A trickle of blood escapes from his nose. His textbook drops to the floor as Sid covers his face with his hands.

Nigel is a foot taller than Sid, and twice as wide. "Mouthful of shit? Shitface Sado-ski. Ha! Cock."

Sid pinches his nose and tries to keep the blood off his clothes. He wonders how many people saw that.

"Dude," says Scott, turning to Sid to assess the damage. "You're alright..." He pulls a P.E. T-shirt from his bag, rips off the sleeve and hands it to his friend.

This is priceless. "Boyfriend going to wipe it up for you?" laughs Nigel.

Scott stares at Nigel, indifferent. For long enough to make the bully feel uncomfortable.

Nigel bounces his football. "What you looking at?"

Sid pushes his glasses back away from his bleeding nose, thankful that they are still in one piece. Last thing he needs. The embarrassment hurts more than the actual punch. He doesn't want Scott to see him like this, the way everyone else sees him. They were doing so well. He'd almost managed to convince Scott he was, well, *normal*.

"So you're the new kid?" assesses Nigel, sidling up to Scott. Close up, the boy is taller than Nigel had imagined. His face has more lines than his age should warrant, as though he hasn't slept a decent night in years. Everything about him is scruffy, but his eyes are as proud as a veteran's.

Scott refuses to indulge him in conversation. He just looks at Nigel, with the steady gaze of an assassin staring through a sniper rifle into the midday sun.

"Hello, hel-lo, anyone in there?" Nigel is spitting the words at Scott now, demanding a reaction, his fist knocking repeatedly against the locker behind Scott's head. Something in the way the new kid is looking at him stops Nigel from actually tapping on his skull, like he usually would.

"Hey," protests Sid, finally finding his voice.

"Shut up Sado," says Nigel quietly. He looks from Scott to Sid and back to Scott. "Freaks," he mutters, and walks away.

The space between Sid and Scott seems suddenly charged with an energy that takes them both by surprise. If they are destined to be friends, then surely this was their first test.

Scott is the first to speak. "He's not very nice."

"He's a prick," spits Sid, unable to hide his hatred.

Scott doesn't miss a beat. Upwards, onwards. "I made up a joke once." He pauses for effect. "What's the highest mountain in the world?"

"What?" asks Sid, puzzled but impressed by Scott's ability to move on from trauma. Maybe it's worth sticking around. Nothing seems to faze this lad.

"Mount Have-a-rest."

Sid stares at him incredulously, before breaking slowly into a smile. It doesn't matter that he doesn't get the joke. They have, it seems, both passed the test after all. It feels like the tiniest tendril, cracking up through the pavement towards sunlight.

"See you later, buddy," says Scott, pushing his earphones onto his head and pressing play.

Scott pulls the headphones from his ears, masterfully erases the frown from his forehead and chases after Sid. "God you're hard to track down!" He jumps playfully on Sid's back.

Sid shakes him off and smiles awkwardly. He'd thought he'd managed to get away. Friends at school is one thing, and he is grateful for the way Scott handled Nigel at lunchtime, but the last thing Sid needs is someone following him home. He picks up the pace.

"You're like that character in that video game, you know, the ghost that's always turning corners, just out of sight. What's that game again?"

Sid has no idea what he's talking about. He doesn't have time for this. His nose is still stinging. He just wants to get home. He should get home. His heavy black lace-ups kick up dust in the path. This is his favourite route home. Beneath them, York Minster looks like a Lego castle and if he closes his eyes for a second, if he can manage to clear his head for just a second, he can imagine what it was like when it was all Vikings and stench. When everyone had to fight for a living, not just the ones whose mums liked a drink.

Scott is relentless. Happy to have survived the first day, he can see the long evening stretching out ahead, the possibilities, the satisfying weight of the DVD in his satchel. The hours to himself. He's curious about the kid walking next to him, hasn't been able to get him out of his mind all day. "You Jewish?" he asks Sid.

Sid frowns. "What? No. Why?"

"Your last name." Scott enunciates the syllables. "Sad-ow-ski".

"That's not Jewish. It's Ukrainian." It feels good to say that, to trace his heritage out loud. Like leaving real footprints, for once.

"You sure it's not Jewish?"

"I'm not Jewish."

Scott's mind moves on. "So, what do you do after school then? For fun?" He pauses to pick up a stone from the path and studies it as they walk.

Sid doesn't wait for him. "Nothing really. I study quite hard. I want to have a career."

"Oh yeah?" Scott struggles to keep in stride with Sid. "What do you want to do?"

Sid instinctively checks behind him, scurries a little faster. "Dunno. Maybe an engineer or something..."

"Engineer? Mt foster dad's an engineer," exclaims Scott, ambling beside his friend, happy to have discovered something in common other than their status as outsiders. "I call him my dad. He's not my real dad. They're my foster parents. But." Scott stops. "I don't think I've ever *told* anyone that."

"Foster parents?" Sid is relieved. He'd assumed Scott came from a 2.4 children cookie-cutter family. In Sid's head, every other family was perfect. Meals around the dinner table, whole conversations, leaving the house together and all that.

Scott nods. "Yeah. Harry Potter I am. He works on big cargo ships. Y'know, travels all over the world on them."

"That's pretty cool." Sid can imagine the stories. The things he'd get to see. He tries to keep his attention on Scott, desperate to steer the conversation away from the topic of parents. He reckons he has about two minutes before he has to be rude to his new friend. Strictly self-preservation. He studies the cracks in the pavement as he walks, and can't help but think of his mum again. The way, as they walked home from the funeral together, she had a meltdown when her bare toes (she had refused to wear the shoes he'd put out for her) touched a crack in the paving slab, and Sid had to run into the pub to get a grown-up to call a taxi and take them home.

"Yeah," continues Scott. "It is for him. I don't get to see him much though. He's always flat out busy." Scott feels the tone getting heavy, doesn't want to scare Sid off just yet. He reaches into his repertoire of voices, pulls out a high-pitched, "You're a wizard, 'arry!" He checks Sid's reaction. "Harry Potter," he clarifies. "Must be like that with your dad?"

Sid thinks on his feet. "Yeah, he's never there. You know we have mocks next week?"

"Why do we do mocks?" questions Scott, frowning. "Why do they make you wait and queue? I hate queuing."

Sid sees the entrance to the snicket up ahead, marking the boundary between his school life and his secrets. Most of the kids at school live on the right side of the alley. They go home to detached houses, at least one car in the driveway, healthy meals and three tellies. The houses on Sid's side of the alley are smaller, ambitions more compressed. People are louder, there is less privacy and everyone buys their meat from Netto. Scott is still talking.

"They tell you to get there at one thirty and then they don't let you go in til two. I think they try and freak you out, play God. It's like when you go to the cinema and you have thirty minutes of trailers. But then again I suppose if the movie is crap then the adverts are the best..."

Sid has no choice but to interrupt. "OK. Bye." He veers off sharply into the alleyway and begins to jog, not wanting to look back. In his bag, the glass bottle clangs rhythmically against his house keys like an alarm clock, as the boarded-up row of shops comes into view. Brick walls and alleyways. An uninspiring environment that would drive most kids crazy with repetition, but Sid likes the claustrophobia of the rabbit warren he's grown up in. It's the wide avenues of the affluent areas of the city that make him nervous. The manor houses with topiary hedges and riverside views. He has grown up with nothing: four inherited walls on a terraced street, an attic full of heirlooms and no new possessions in nearly a decade. He's grown into the containment. He knows his place.

Baffled, Scott remains at the end of the alley surprised by how quickly his new friend is running away from him. Sid is stronger than he looks. "See you then," he says to no-one. He turns back towards the main road.

CHAPTER 2

Nanda's is the kind of shop that has been destroyed so often that there's barely anything left to steal. Its half-filled shelves give it a post-apocalyptic starkness that appeals to Sid's pessimistic streak. In such a sad place, his secret feels safe. Still, he skirts around the perimeter of the aisles, unconvincingly inspecting the Armageddon-proof tins of condensed milk, double-checking reflections in the broken mirrors to make sure he is alone.

Mr Nanda crosses his arms across his knitted tank top and waits for the school boy to acknowledge him. Sidney's been coming into the shop for God knows how long and he can still barely muster a hello. When the boy does make eye contact, it's furtive and brief. He is always alone. Mr Nanda is used to the cheeky camaraderie of his own teenage nephews, second-generation chancers who don't know how lucky they have it. This lad, with his relentless frown, makes Mr Nanda nervous. "Last time again?" he asks.

The corner shop has become one of the few places where Sid feels purposeful: there is only ever one product on his shopping list and he doesn't need to ask for it. He takes the empty bottle from his school bag and places it on the counter. For these thirty seconds of each day, in the moments of transaction between replenishment, his bag feels light. He manages a brief glance towards the shopkeeper as he hands over the money, exact to the penny. It strikes Sid as funny that even bootleg vodka, the kind of liquor that hasn't conformed to any regulatory standards, that would surely fail every taste test that the industry could throw at it, is priced at £4.99. As though it's a really good deal. Why not just call it a fiver? Still, he's damned if he'll give a penny more than necessary to the bastards who make it. Sid counts out his change down to the last copper, every time. "Thanks," he mumbles, as he shoves the new bottle of unbranded vodka deep into his bag. He doesn't hang around. Lately, he has the impression that Mr Nanda has something to say to him. Sid has a feeling he knows what it is, and it's the last thing he wants to hear.

At the door, Sid almost collides with someone entering the shop. It's rare you see a new face around here, but Sid's certain this man isn't a local. Let's be honest: if you weren't from here, you'd steer well clear of this shop. It has shithole written all over it. Literally. In six-foot high letters, misspelt, on the north-facing wall. Sid looks at the man. Mid-forties, salt and pepper stubble, a receding hairline and a slick suit. Sid has an eye for detail. He steps aside to let the man pass, and scurries outside.

Well aware of the tiny space he takes up in the world, Sid is used to going unnoticed. Which is why it unnerves him to feel the stranger's gaze on the back of his school blazer, a good ten seconds after he's left Nanda's. There is nothing captivating about Sid's presence. No need to take a second look. He isn't handsome. Not tall. His eyes are a muddy puddle of green and brown. No one would say that Sid Sadowskyj was cool, or interesting, or fun. Growing up in Yorkshire, he has the impression that the most unique thing about him is his name, and that's also the thing he hates most. Sadowskyj was his father's name, and his father hasn't shown his face since Sid was six months old.

He steps carefully over the litter, strewn across the narrow track at the back of the shop, manoeuvres himself deftly through the hole in the metal fence, careful not to catch his clothes on the barbed wire. Across the scorched patch of grass, he can see the rows of terraced houses stretching out down the hill. Somewhere, amidst the grid of back streets and satellite dishes, is his house, and within that his mum's bedroom, and within that his mum, and within that her impossible, stubborn mind. Karen Sadowskyj. Female. 38 years old. Libran. He opens her post, he signs her forms, he can forge her signature down to the last flourish, but he never has a clue what the hell she's thinking.

What's in a name? He's read that line a hundred times, revising for English Literature. For Sid, Sadowskyj is the name of a strong Ukrainian man who read all of the classics and took photographs and could read music and left his wife and baby boy and his Polaroid camera as though it was all worth nothing. Sid wishes he could remember him. Often, he has the impression that the memories he has are not his own. With his mother refusing to talk on the subject and nobody else around to ask, Sid has created a back story in which his dad is always majestic, always loyal, always loving. A lovable rogue, a free spirit. Where his dad plays the guitar, sad Eastern songs around a campfire and where Sid's mum is still young and still painting and there's fire in their bellies and love in their hearts. In his version of the story, Sid's dad has just left for a while, to find himself or to earn some money or to get himself together or whatever adults do. He's not in prison, or a junkie, or dead, or any of the other things that people try to tell him. As a kid, Sid would spend whole days looking out of his bedroom window, waiting for his dad to come home, as though he'd just nipped out to the shops. Once, while his mum lay comatose on the sofa downstairs, Sid stole a peek inside the ornate, out-of-bounds wooden box she kept on her dressing table. He'd seen a photo of a bottle-green VW Beetle, convinced himself that this was his dad's car, that this was the chariot that would roll back into town one sunny afternoon, laden with love and presents. Salvation!

As the days bled into years, the time between his mum's binges evened out into a constant state of miserable, unignorable alcoholism that led Sid away from his childhood and towards a new reality. He took to the role like a fish to water, his kindness towards his mum genuine and inherent. He stopped asking to go to birthday parties, stopped even being invited. Learned that if he stood on a chair he could hide the razor blades on top of the wardrobe; how much cereal he needed to survive for a week. He packed his own school bag, kissed his mum goodbye, kept his head down and got on with the task of growing up and that was that.

He gave up trying to make friends and resigned himself to always being the weird kid. He tried to track down his dad through the library archives, and he gave up on that too and started writing letters instead. One letter, addressed to his dad, every time things got too much. Today was one of those days. Too many distractions to his usual routine, and Sid picks up his pace as he treads across the grass, wanting to put distance between himself and the stranger in the corner shop. It was nothing. So someone looked at him funny. That was hardly unusual. He's sure it was nothing.

He dodges the washing lines strung out across his back street and unlatches the wooden gate. Theirs is the house with the peeling paint. It's not that the houses either side are fancy, far from it, but Sid is well aware that his own house screams neglect. There used to be an apple tree in the back yard, but even that has given up the ghost. Sid prefers this back route, since the front of the house opens straight onto the street and is always an obstacle course of random neighbours and awkward hellos. It makes more sense to come in this way. Besides, his mum's bedroom is at the front of the house, and the longer Sid can let her sleep, the better it is for both of them. He closes the gate quietly behind him and crosses the faded flagstones to the yellow door at the back of the house. The yard is tiny, and sometimes Sid can't help but feel jealous of the big back gardens up near the school, where you could just sit and be, where no-one would be twitching at the net curtains next door to see what you're up to. Last summer he tried to coax his mum into their back yard. Crazy hot and he thought it might be a first step, the healing heat of the sun on her skin, a good half-way point between the house and the rest of the world. But she refused to get dressed and stood shivering in the doorway in her bra and knickers, watching Sid pulling out the weeds from between the flagstones until he got embarrassed and told her to just go back inside, please. He glances around the yard. The pebble-dash is flaking off the back wall and there's bird shit caked to the roof of the old coal shed, a relic from when his grandad kept racing pigeons in the sixties. He kicks angrily at the pile of ash on the floor; his mum's been smoking in his room again. He turns his key and shoulder-barges the stiff back door.

He hangs up his keys on the hook and checks the fridge for signs of life. The milk is a centimetre lower than when he left this morning, and there is a used cereal bowl in the sink. Sid smiles. Perhaps he worries too much. He unlaces his shoes and places them neatly by the back door, before tidying away the open packet of cornflakes on the counter. These minor victories, some food in her stomach, they all count for something.

Their small living room is an homage to red. The carpet is a garish intersection of crimson flowers and paisley, a style which could only have been fashionable in the seventies and which provided Sid with hours of fun as a toddler with a Matchbox car. His nanna used to say it hid a multitude of sins, the carpet. Now, Sid no longer notices the pattern. It's amazing the things you get used to. In the same way, he forgets that the gas fire, a brass-effect monstrosity in the centre of one wall, was ever functional. The porcelain dancing ladies and colourful Poole pottery that used to line the mantelpiece were packed into boxes years ago, and the only adornment now is a cut-glass ashtray full to the brim. Sid swipes it and pads back to the kitchen. He hears her bedroom light switch on and off and on and off and on and off again. He'd better make a start on her food.

For all that Karen is indifferent to the outside world, she is extremely particular when it comes to controlling the objects in her own house. Though the cupboards in the kitchen are full of mismatched vintage china, Sid knows better than to touch. Instead, he sticks to his mum's instructions. There are only ever the same two mugs, plates and sets of cutlery in use. Sid's fine with the set-up. Less stuff to wash up. The rule doesn't apply to glasses, though. Always several glasses, always a glass within reach.

He takes her favourite plate from the drying rack. Dusty rose with a fine line of gold around the edge. The thinness of the china makes Sid nervous every time he handles it. He has the impression that this kind of crockery should only be used on special occasions, which are rarely celebrated around here. The formica counter top is stained but clean. Sid assembles the ingredients for the sandwich without commotion. Peanut butter. Two slices of white bread. An under-ripe tomato. He spreads peanut butter on the bread, right up to the corners, arranges four slices of tomato so that they do not overlap. He studies the finished work and decides to carefully cut off the crusts, making a perfect square. Finally, he cuts his masterpiece diagonally and places it on the plate. Their kitchen is ill-equipped in many respects, but they have a hoard of certain objects. Besides a cabinet full of retro kitchenware that would make a collector weep, Sid's nanna had a penchant for trays.

He selects a tacky, kitsch round tray with basket edging and kittens on it. The waft of cigarette smoke drifts down the stairs from his mum's bedroom.

Sid composes himself. "Do you have a clean glass?" he shouts.

No answer.

He takes an amber glass from the drying rack and sets it on the tray next to the plate. Deftly, he slings his bag over one shoulder and heads for the stairs.

The wall to the right of the narrow steps up is lined with family portraits of happier times. Over the years, some of the frames have been smashed in anger, and they hang wonkily on their fittings. Every time Sid goes upstairs it takes all of his willpower not to realign them. He has taken to climbing two steps at a time, so he has less chance to be bothered by the lack of symmetry. Even with the tray, he has it down to a fine art.

At the top of the stairs Sid pauses outside a closed bedroom door. He balances the tray against the door frame and knocks three times. He waits a second before nudging the door open with his foot.

She's been chain smoking as usual. The room swirls with dust and smoke, dark except for a bluing shaft of light that dissects the double bed. At the window, the once-white lace curtains are the yellow of old tea. Sid takes a few steps and places the tray on the bedside table. Its old legs wobble under the weight.

"Mum," he half-whispers.

Beneath several layers of crocheted shawls and heavy wool blankets draped over the bed, a tiny figure buries its head further out of sight.

"Turn the light off," moans Karen.

"It's off." Sid pulls the bottle of vodka from his schoolbag, unscrews the lid and pours a glassful.

Karen stirs slightly at the familiar sound of glass on glass.

"It's all there for you." Sid reaches out towards the bed, then thinks better of it; smooths his hand over the surface of the quilted bedspread instead. It used to be his mum's pride and joy, years ago, she used to say the colours made her happy, but it's all tattered threads now. "I'll see you in a bit," he says, as he closes her bedroom door behind him.

In his own room, the contrast is noticeable. Sid exhales loudly. The walls are white and wood-chipped, a blank canvas that most teenagers would deface in an instant. But Sid prefers them bare. Compared to the chintz and inherited busyness of every other room, his space feels almost lunar calm. He might own nothing but it's his nothing. He unpacks his school bag. That's why it pisses him off so much when his mum comes in here to smoke. Sure, it's a better view. If you squint, you can see the purple heather on the moors in the distance, and it means she gets a few breaths of fresh air between drags. But it always feels like an invasion of privacy, the fact she comes in when he's not here, even though he has nothing to hide. Sid stacks his textbooks on the dressing table and gives the room a quick scan. Sometimes, he gets the feeling that she's been moving things around. The flash on the Polaroid camera on his window sill will be facing left instead of right, or his yellow revision notes will be stuck on to the mirror less firmly than when he left. His mum's interest baffles him. In a house where everything is a relic, Sid's bedroom has the least to offer.

He closes the pale green curtains and undresses systematically, laying out first his blazer, then his trousers, then his school shirt on the single bed. As he hangs up his school uniform on the curtain pole, Sid remembers the blackcurrant stain on his shirt cuff and he makes a mental note to give it a scrub after tea. In a second, he'll open the window as wide as it goes and leave it like that until morning, in an always-futile attempt to stop his uniform from smelling like home. He's taught himself to just grin and bear the cold, to sleep through the shivers, even in mid-winter.

Standing in front of the wardrobe, Sid selects his clothes as though he's about to step onto a catwalk. A white polo shirt is chosen and dismissed (the collar won't lie flat and he can't be bothered to iron tonight). The time it takes him to choose, you'd think the wardrobe was full. In truth, there are only four T-shirts that fit, a couple of jumpers and a choice between two pairs of jeans, one stonewash blue, one a darker shade, both too small. The rest of the wardrobe is taken up by polythene bags covering old dresses and his grandad's boiler suit. At the back of the wardrobe is a painting that Karen did years ago, that Sid is afraid to remind her of. He pulls a pale blue polo shirt from its hanger, wriggles into jeans and combs his hair.

Shit, he thinks. Almost forgot. The letter is still in his school bag. He checks it over, smoothing out the creased corners. Still legible. He sits down cross-legged beside his bed and reaches underneath the pine slats. Careful not to make a noise, he pulls out a large hard-backed guitar case. He silences the springs as he clicks it open. Inside, the lining is red velvet and the acoustic guitar long gone. Sid doesn't ever remember music in his house. The radio, sure, his mum humming, of course, but not actual music, the live kind that he imagines gets right under your skin to the core of things. He places today's letter in the guitar-shaped space with the others and slides the case back under the bed.

Downstairs again, Sid turns the dial on the radio until it clicks. It's angled on the living room windowsill, propped up by a leather-bound Ukrainian dictionary, spine to the glass, that Sid found under the sink one day. Sid's drilled it into his mum that the radio has to stay in this position, the only place where the signal is strong enough, and it's the only possession that she never seems to disturb. Sid has it on good authority that Karen used to love to dance. He's seen the evidence and photographs don't lie. There are dresses in her wardrobe that support the theory.

Sid craves company. He fills his evenings with the voices of strangers: talk shows and phone-ins and agony aunts. He's not really interested in Radio 1 or the Sunday Chart Show. What's the point in spending all that time learning lyrics if you don't have anyone to discuss them with? He'd rather have common sense, old wives' tales, the kindness of strangers. Stories that reach across the airwaves fully formed, with a beginning, middle and end.

He puts his knife and fork together on his empty plate and pats his stomach, convincing himself he is full. Then, without thinking, he stands up suddenly and begins to re-tune the radio. He's not exactly sure what he's looking for. It sounds stupid, but he wants to have something to talk to Scott about tomorrow. And Scott had been listening to classical music. Sid fiddles with the frequency. That is, if Scott ever wants to speak to him again. The radio static gets suddenly louder and he crosses the room, closes the door. But what else could Sid have done? There are rules, routines. Things have to be done at a certain time. Sid wants to tell Scott, he'd have loved to have spent all evening wandering around town like everyone else does. McDonalds, the arcades in the cinema until closing time. Small talk with girls. But that's not his life, it never has been. The sound of a piano concerto tinkles through the static. Later, Sid will neatly fold a blanket on the back step and sit out there. Once the alcohol has had time to work and he's peeked in on his mum to check that she's out for the count, once his homework is done, Sid will turn the radio up and look at the stars and try to think about nothing. But for now, there is housework to be done and a stain to remove and the radio can be nothing more than background noise. He picks up his plate and returns to the kitchen.

CHAPTER 3

Scott kicks the covers from his double bed. His legs are flailing against his will and he wakes to find his body drenched in sweat. He lies still, startled by his own strength, staring up at the collage of faces glued to his ceiling, which look molten and nightmarish in the half-light. He can hear his heart drumming against his rib cage. He draws his knees up to his chest and reminds himself to breathe.

There is a repetitive thud at the base of his skull, like a baseball player preparing to pitch. He scrunches his eyes tightly closed. There'd been music in his dream, a kind of relentless drum and bass, with high frequency screams that Scott couldn't be certain weren't his own voice. It always takes him a while to navigate back into reality. He waits for the thudding to merge with the rhythm of his breath. Through the wall, he can hear the steady Neanderthal wheeze of his foster dad snoring. Maybe Scott hadn't been screaming after all.

The clock on his desk illuminates 03:07 in green digits. He turns his head to look outside, half expecting to see Biblical storms, lightning cracking across a fluorescent sky, something to justify his terror, at least. But the cul-de-sac of Birchhill Brae is sleeping. Scott wonders how they manage it. He's become almost violent in his desire for company. Most evenings, he finds himself standing at the window, scanning the detached houses opposite for signs of life, not giving a damn what the neighbours think. Once midnight comes, he can forget solidarity. No one stirs, no lights switch on and no sleepy figures microwave Horlicks through the slatted blinds of their pristine kitchens. There is nothing to minimise Scott's crippling sense of absolute isolation. At times, looking across at the uniform, polished estate cars and manicured hedges from here to the main road, Scott wonders if his neighbours are droids. The faux-Victorian street lamp that his foster dad has put up in the front garden shines its intrusive light in through the bay window. Scott forgot to close the curtains again. He claws cautiously at his legs, still wary of his surroundings, struggling to extrapolate the nightmare from the waking. Tonight, there was a dog. Snarl-mouthed and blood-red eyeballs, on a too-long leash. He remembers reading about a link between black dogs and depression. Something to do with Churchill. He blinks hard.

Swinging his legs to the side of his bed, he feels the wetness on the sheet and his torment turns instantly to shame. "Shit," he blurts out, his panic heightening as he jumps out of the bed. In no order, he begins to grab at the objects littering his duvet cover, the debris of another evening spent alone. He piles it all onto the floor: an autobiography of the Dalai Lama, its spine broken; a well-thumbed copy of Time magazine with the Twin Towers on the front; and seven back issues of Empire magazine, with pages ripped from the centre spreads. Then, he takes a deep breath and peels the bed sheets away from the mattress. He swears again. It's soaked right through.

The thick beige carpet cushions his frustrated steps as he trudges past his parents' bedroom, past the spare bedrooms, and spirals his way down the elaborate staircase. On nights like this, the detached house feels too grand and Scott feels himself shrink within the luxury.

The contents of the house are too polished for his state of mind, making a mockery of how difficult he finds it sometimes just to exist. He craves the scrape of bare brick on the back of his hand, rough edges, the unforgiving harshness of the moorland. Sensations that bring the blood to the surface, not the marble and taffeta of middle class decor. This place has never felt like home. Maybe that's why he can't settle: Scott refuses to accept that a building like this could contain his whole world. It's not that he tries to be difficult. It's just... He jumps down the last two steps. There is far too much to fight against. Although Malcolm and Elaine are the only parents he's ever known, Scott still feels at times like an intruder in their lives. He wishes he could be better for them. When they signed up to take on someone else's kid, they had probably hoped for so much more.

In the utility room, he bundles his sheets into the washing machine then, as an afterthought, steps quickly out of his boxer shorts and flings them in as well. The washing powder pours out of its box too quickly, cascading his hands in sickly-sweet powder and Scott swears without meaning to. He stabs at some buttons until the machine emits a satisfying swoosh. As the suds begin to erase the evidence, he starts to calm down a little.

Down here, at the back of the house, he can almost pretend to be alone. He draws back the curtains at the conservatory windows, unlocks the door and steps out into the garden. The freshly-mown grass soaks the soles of his feet, and he is glad for the sudden stab of coldness that jolts up through his body. He ignores the signs of cultivation that his foster dad insists on imposing - the irritating water feature that trickles all night, the two stone lions on either side of the shed, the ridiculous pagoda at the end of the lawn - and looks up instead.

Even the sky seems less expansive here. When they first moved into the city, Scott would creep down in the middle of the night with his astrology book and scrutinise the sky, wondering where all the constellations had gone. It seemed impossible, too cynical even for Scott, that the universe should perhaps shrink to accommodate his mum's naivety. He thought he must be looking in the wrong place. It took him the best part of a month to accept that, in the city, this was just the way things were. You couldn't even look up and see the stars.

Scott rubs at his temple. He still can't believe she took him back again. Two affairs that she knows of and Scott knows she's not stupid enough to believe there weren't others. He scoffs. His foster dad was always a let-down. Malcolm Elliott, world-class engineer, balding sleaze, prize arsehole. Scott was just glad they weren't bound by blood. After the first time he'd walked out, they'd done alright, Scott and his mum, made a good life out in that tiny house in the countryside. His mum, Elaine, had cut her hair short and started wearing the clothes that she wanted to, and Scott had made friends at school for the first time ever. He scans the sky and fails to find Venus. It didn't last long. His dad turned up again a year later, carrying a red rose and a designer dress for Elaine, as though it was her who should make more of an effort. And she took the bait. Over the years, Elaine learned to forgive. Her hair grew long again, they went on all-inclusive holidays to far-away places that his father couldn't even pronounce. Scott found that their cottage became full of new gadgets and expensive gifts designed to placate, as Malcolm pissed his scent all over the place, marking his territory. His mum was a sucker for it all, convincing herself that it was just a one-off, that that's the point of marriage, isn't it, to stick it out, for better or worse.

And then his dad did it all over again. Only this time, it wasn't a stranger, it was his bleach-blonde secretary just out of uni, and it wasn't in hotels on business trips, it was twice a week in his marital bed, while Elaine was at work and Scott was trying to make an effort at school. And his mum promised Scott that this time it was over. And then Malcolm turned up again with the keys to a new house in "the best part of York", and the promise of loyalty. And that was how they had ended up here in this shitty cul-de-sac with too much stuff and Scott couldn't even see the stars. Sometimes he wished they would just give him back.

"What the hell are you doing?" Elaine's voice is an incredulous hiss.

Scott turns around. In the same instant, he realises he has been sitting in the middle of the lawn, cross-legged, completely naked. He stands up quickly. "Nothing, mum. Just." He shuffles awkwardly towards the house.

Elaine stares at her son. "What's going on?"

"Nothing, mum. I just needed some fresh air." Scott grabs a fresh pair of pyjama bottoms from a pile of ironed laundry.

"Stark naked, in the garden, for all the neighbours to see?" His mum is disgusted. She tightens the belt on her white dressing gown. "Your dad has to be off in two hours," she says, double locking the conservatory door. "Don't you dare wake him up."

"Sorry." Scott checks the digital display on the washing machine.

"Just keep quiet," spits his mum, her patience already lost. "You can sort those out in the morning. I don't know why you keep doing it. It's disgusting." She stares at her son for a few seconds longer, wondering whether to tell him how she really feels, that she would happily surrogate him for a stranger. That at least with a stranger she wouldn't feel the *obligation*, she wouldn't feel the constant need to try to understand an alien life-form. She'd always hoped she could be a guiding light, believed it needn't be a matter of genetic likeness, that her good heart would see her through whatever this blue-eyed kid could throw at her. It had been her idea. She points at the barefoot green smears on the kitchen flagstones. "And clean the floor before you go back to bed."

Scott looks down at his feet and nods as Elaine tuts and trots up the stairs.

In the darkness, Scott's mind is racing. The American interviewer is sitting at the kitchen counter, as though he has been there all along, eating Cheerios straight from the box. His voice is unmistakably accusatory. *And at what point,* he sneers, *did you realise that you were unloved?* Scott glares momentarily at the empty chair, reaches for the kitchen towel and attacks the floor in an attempt to shut up the voice. That's easy, Scott thinks. I was born unloved. It's practically written on my birth certificate.

Back upstairs, he systematically arranges black bin liners on top of his mattress, gets into bed in the way that makes the least noise. In the stillness of the night, every sound is exaggerated. He reaches carefully down for the remote control and presses play. The TV above his bed is on Mute, but, as the images of 'The Godfather' play out on the screen, Scott mouths the words by heart. Suddenly, he hears a voice that is out of place. Malcolm is awake.

Scott presses pause on the DVD and lies motionless, startled, waiting for what will happen next. His dad is furious.

"I can't get back to bloody sleep now, can I. For Christ's sake, Elaine."

Scott closes his eyes. A loud bang on his bedroom door shocks him upright.

"Fourteen years old, on his fifth school and still pissing the bed!"

Scott stares at the ceiling. The tears that come are effortless and unstoppable, staining streams down his cheeks. He can taste the salt. He pulls the covers up over his head, blocking out everything except the film. Real life has never given him what he needs. On the screen, Don Corleone is staring at Sonny in the mortuary. Look how they massacred my boy, he is about to say.

CHAPTER 4

Blackfriars High has a school yard that reminds Scott of every prison film he's ever watched. Full of individuals afraid to be themselves. He sits on the high wall, bouncing his ball against the red stone. His aim is precise. It has to be. The wall is only a foot wide and he doesn't fancy going down into the yard to retrieve it. It isn't so much that Scott thinks he is better than everyone else. Rather, he knows that he will be. Being liked has never been on his agenda.

"This is paradise. This is paradise, I'm tellin' you," he sneers out loud. Scott doesn't bother with the accent. He always finds it easier to remember lines from films if he absorbs them completely, co-opts them into his character and speaks with his own voice, so that, at times like this, he *is* Tony Montana. "All I have in this world is my balls and my word, and I don't break 'em for no one."

Scott is oblivious to the looks. He has always stood out. Even when he was little, his parents could never really figure out why. At lunchtimes he eats the same junk as everyone else. He doesn't have asthma, he doesn't smell funny and he can swim five lengths underwater if he has to. It's in his bones, this rebellion against what he's told to think, say, do or be. Always has been. The thing that gets people talking about Scott is something more fundamental than surface: a barrier that only Sid has been permitted to cross.

From his perch, Scott scans the classroom for his friend. The science block is a modern glass extension haphazardly grafted onto the side of the old building, below the wall where Scott sits. Nothing about the design lends itself to education: in summer the place becomes a greenhouse; in winter an ice box. He can see Sid seated at the back, the only pupil copying down notes while the teacher's back is turned to the board. His blazer hangs neatly on the back of his chair.

It isn't that Scott dislikes school. It doesn't make him miserable, or angry. That's the problem: it doesn't make him anything. It strikes him as so neutral that he can't see the point. School is just a way to mark the daytime hours. Everything he needs to know, Scott finds out for himself.

He swings his legs over the side of the wall and jumps into the yard, landing just as the end-of-class bell rings.

"Sidney!" Scott bounces the ball towards the entrance of the science block.

Sid grins, stopping the ball with his foot and nervously kicking it back. "Get up to much last night?" he asks Scott, pulling on his blazer.

It is one of those days in late spring, the week after a warm one, where the temperature drops suddenly and everyone remembers that summer's not quite here yet. Scott's blazer is still on his bed at home. If he tries hard enough, he can convince himself he isn't cold. Mind over matter. "This and that," he mumbles. His head is still reeling. He'd been listening to music on the walk to school, a Rachmaninoff concerto, but even that had been too much. He walks in silence with Sid to their next class. When they reach the classroom, Scott realises that, if he doesn't make an effort soon, they might never speak again. It seems like Sid could exist forever in a vacuum, that it wouldn't take much for him to retreat into his shell and Scott doesn't want that. "You?" he says abruptly. "You get up to anything last night?"

Sid shifts his bag so that Scott can sit down at the desk next to him. "Nowt much. Just the usual," he says, smiling. It was true, nothing out-of-the-ordinary had happened to Sid last night. He'd listened to Classic FM until late, had his usual shower, checked in on his mum and made her a slice of toast and went to bed. But he'd woken up in a great mood. Even the morning check on his mum, the usual minor battle with Karen over removing the empty vodka bottle hadn't dampened his optimism, and he'd arrived at school with a spring in his step. He'd even used the main entrance. But it seemed too forward to tell Scott any of that now. Scott clearly wasn't in the mood for talking. A couple of times, Sid tries to make conversation, asking Scott how his revision is going, asking him if he has an extra copy of 'East of Eden' that Mrs Finn recommended. Scott's answers are curt and, after a while, Sid gives up and lines up his stationery instead.

Scott wishes he could humour him, but right now the only thing he can manage is to stare straight ahead and focus on the beat that still lingers in his head. His eyes are stinging-sore and he's dreading the moment the teacher asks him to remove his shades. Days like this, after evenings like that, Scott feels exposed. His eyes have always given him away. Days like this, it takes something special to heal him. More likely than not, he'll shamble through the day, speak to no-one and go to sleep feeling as shitty when he closes his eyes as he did when he opened them. He'll pray that tonight will be different. He wonders how long his mum will give him the silent treatment for.

Scott stares blankly at the boy next to him. There's something of an old-school gentleman about Sid. The way his hair is always combed into a neat side parting. The fact that his glasses are NHS milk-bottle-thick. Every mark Sid makes on the page in front of him is deliberate and measured, like a senior draftsman drawing blueprints for a space rocket. He even smells like an old person, that musty mix of stale air and tinned food that, if he's honest, repulses Scott a little. Sid seems able to withstand Scott's stare for longer than most people. When he looks up from his revision notes, it is with a gentle curiosity. There is no malice behind his eyes, just a persistent melancholia. He gives Scott a thin smile.

Scott tugs at his sunglasses. "Have you ever seen 'Groundhog Day'?" he asks Sid, as their classmates pile in.

Sid shakes his head, a little taken aback by his classmate's bloodshot eyes which seem like an unexpected chink in Scott's armour. In his pocket is the pen that he bought Scott this morning, to replace the one he threw away. Sid twiddles his grip around the plastic, suddenly reluctant to hand it over. He doesn't want to give Scott the wrong idea. He glances at the items on the desk in front of Scott: he doesn't have a notebook, ruler or a pen. What the hell, thinks Sid, and he nervously edges the new pen onto Scott's desk. "You can borrow this if you want," he suggests, tentatively.

Scott looks blankly at the cheap, plastic pen on the desk in front of him. It's one of those with four colours of ink, that you push down to select depending on your mood. He presses forcefully on red and a piece of plastic snaps away. He turns to Sid accusingly. "Where'd you get this piece of crap?" he sneers. "Back of a lorry?"

Sid laughs, thinking he's joking.

"It's not funny." Scott is genuinely angry. "How am I meant to write with this?" He hunches forward in his chair and rests his head on his arms, fully aware of how unreasonable he's being, but unable to stop.

Removing her pastel pink jacket, Mrs Finn watches the interaction carefully. She has always felt a certain fondness for the Polish kid. Polish, yes, she's sure she'd heard that somewhere. A dad behind bars. Not that she got into teaching for the care of waifs and strays. But there were certain kids who you just knew didn't really stand a hope in hell of improving their station in life, no matter how hard they tried. She watches as Sid aligns the yellow highlighter perfectly perpendicular to his ruler. Poor Sidney, with his post-war haircut, his pitiful posture and his mum who never makes it to Parents Evening. Mrs Finn is sure that Sid's intentions are good, that he really believes he will get into university but, truth be told, Mrs Finn can't see him doing much more than answering phones for a living. Being a polite, tiny cog in a more important machine. As for the new kid, well, let's just say she can see why all the other schools wanted rid of him.

"You alright there, Mr Elliott? Sit up straight, you can lounge in your lunch break."

Scott glares at his teacher and buries his forehead further into his arms.

"OK," snaps Mrs Finn, making a mental note of his insolence but not feeling up to the fight. She projects her voice to the back of the class. "As you may have noticed, spring has sprung and the birds are singing. Can anybody tell me what this means?" She fans her face dramatically as she waits for a response.

Lucy Rogan, a lanky girl with wild curls and a henna tattoo on the back of her hand, speaks up in a husky voice. "Cider in the park?" she suggests.

The class laughs. Sid smiles to himself. Without even looking at Lucy, he knows that the turquoise nail varnish on her left hand is slightly less perfect than her right. He's fancied her since primary school.

Scott half-heartedly raises his forearm.

"Yes, Mr Elliott?"

"It means," says Scott, with great effort. "The end is in sight."

Mrs Finn nods. "Exactly," she says. "To expand on your new classmate's very succinct observation, the end of your time in this school, indeed in any secondary school, is drawing to a close. That does not mean you take your foot off the gas. The decisions you make this term will define your whole life. Whether you work hard or not over the next couple of months, for your mock exams and eventually for your GCSEs proper, will determine whether you spend the rest of your lives as a supermarket cashier..." Mrs Finn's eyes fall instinctively on Sid before she continues, "...or as a professional like myself."

Scott notices the rip in the back of his teacher's tights as she makes hawk-circles around the room. It's all surface, he thinks. He wants to scream at her that she's nothing special. Passing through so many schools, Scott has become quick to identify the difference between sincerity and superiority. Mrs Finn, with her shrill, self-righteous way of addressing people younger than herself, makes Scott's blood boil. He bets she's had an ad in the soulmates section of the local newspaper for the past ten years and that she genuinely wonders why no one ever calls. Scott zones out.

"Today, I want you all to stop day-dreaming and think seriously about what you will do once that final bell rings on the 12th of July." Mrs Finn tries not to sound too enthusiastic. She's booked her month in Provence already and is counting down the days. "This morning you'll be pulled out of the lesson to see the careers advisor. Her time is valuable, so I want you to mentally prepare yourselves for it. You only have a few minutes with her, so let's have a good think about what you want to do. OK?"

Sid shuffles in his seat. Easy. He wants to go to university. Make a load of friends and never look back.

Mrs Finn scans the room. "Christopher Babbage, let's start with you. What would you like to do for a job when you leave school?"

Babbage fumbles with his shirt sleeve. A small caricature of a boy, caught like a rabbit in headlights. "Erm. Plumber, Miss?"

"Hmm. A plumber." Mrs Finn smiles slightly out of the side of her mouth, trying to imagine this meek follower of a boy maintaining a successful rapport with clients. "Why a plumber?"

"Just." Babbage recoils a little under pressure.

"How much do you think you will earn?" pushes Mrs Finn.

"About thirty thousand pounds, Miss?"

"Well," concedes the teacher, "with what plumbers charge, I don't think that will be a problem."

The room laughs.

"Right. Lucy, what about you?"

Lucy looks up from her notebook where she has been lost in a world of random doodles and scribbles.

"Any ideas?"

Lucy concentrates and stares at her teacher through intense green eyes. "Nails, Miss," she states confidently. "A nail beautician."

"Nails. Ambitious." Mrs Finn smirks and flicks through the register on her clipboard. "Let's see if you can squeeze that C minus in geography to a C?"

"Nice," says Lucy. "I'll get you a discount, Miss."

Scott turns to Sid. "Why does she need a C in geography to be a nail beautician?" he wonders aloud.

Sid shrugs his shoulders, relieved that Scott is still talking to him.

Noticing Scott speaking out of turn, Mrs Finn steals her opportunity for revenge. "How about our new student. Mr Elliott, grace us with your wisdom. What would you like to be when you're older?" She walks over to Scott's desk and picks up the handout she distributed at the beginning of the class. Scott has covered the entire two sides in elaborate graphic drawings. She holds the A4 paper by its corner, as though afraid to touch it. "Sorry, did I interrupt you?"

"No, Miss." He reaches up to take back his design, but Mrs Finn raises her hand out of reach.

"You need to concentrate in my class. I'd love to see what's more interesting than your future as an employee." She studies Scott's artwork. The marks on the paper are predictably erratic, as though he couldn't decide on one course of action or even one pen colour. "What is *this*?"

Scott is embarrassed. "Well, it's a scene from 'Lost Highway' but I reversed the angle and..."

Mrs Finn glares at him, unimpressed.

"Well it's not just revered, sorry reversed..."

From the back of the class comes Nigel Ball's voice. "Faggot!" he yells.

"That's enough, Mr Ball. Scott..." She looks at her clipboard. "You have been to umpteen schools, on target for..." she raises her eyebrows. "...Ds and a C if you're lucky. So what do you think you will do when you leave school?"

Scott doesn't have to think. "I'm going to make movies, Miss. And travel." He feels enthusiastic for the first time all morning. "Just keep making the best films I can." He anticipates her next question. "Earn maybe three hundred thousand pounds a year."

Sid's eyes widen as laughter ricochets from the windows. Mrs Finn joins in, until it dawns on her that the only person not laughing is Scott. "Are you serious?"

"Yes, Miss," replies Scott, not flinching.

Mrs Finn places the artwork back on Scott's desk. She dusts her hands together and walks briskly to her own desk at the front of the class, peels a clean blue sheet from her notepad and begins to write. "I think it would be good for you to see the Head Teacher."

Scott frowns.

"You're not in trouble. Here." She hands him the note.

Scott begins to unfold it.

"No, no, you don't need to read it. Give it to Mr Olsen. Do you know where his office is?"

Scott nods and hoists his satchel onto his shoulder. As he walks towards the door, he pauses at Lucy's desk. "You have great nails," he whispers kindly, with a tired smile.

"Now class," he hears Mrs Finn say, as he pulls the door closed behind him. "Let's have some serious answers."

The class erupts in laughter as Scott lets the door slam loudly behind him. He considers heading straight home. Fuck Olsen. But he is curious.

Olsen's office is the perfect location for dreams to be annihilated. The top floor room is so full of Olsen's accolades to his own minor achievements that there is no space for anyone else's. Scott has the feeling he could walk in here wearing an Olympic gold medal and it would be relegated to a bottom drawer. He takes a seat opposite his headteacher, studies the neat line of framed diplomas on the grand wooden desk in front of him. Not a speck of dust to be found on any of them. It's Olsen's pride and joy.

Mr Olsen studies the note and tries to decide how best to proceed. He'd reluctantly agreed to take on the Elliott boy. With only two months to go til the end of term, it seemed cruel to say no. Besides, Marcus at St Jude's was an old school pal, and he owed him a favour. Now he wonders if he made the wrong decision. He chooses his words carefully, drawing on the tactics learned at the assertive management training course he attended in Coventry last weekend. "The problem," he begins slowly, "with aiming for the sky is that you will land with a bump. It's excellent and..." Mr Olsen twiddles his thumbs, "*commendable* to have a positive outlook, but look at your grades."

Scott keeps his eyes glued to the headmaster's, still not entirely sure why he's been sent up here. In his last school, he was told off for not participating. Now it seems he's said too much. The headmaster is struggling, tripping over his words despite his best efforts. Scott can tell that this is the part of his job that he hates: that, if Olsen had his way, he'd spend all day alone in his office completing online training courses, and drive home in a soft-top MG at four on the dot every day. Human interaction doesn't come naturally to him.

"Ds and a possible C. Look at you as a person. Four schools in four years." Olsen catches his breath. "Do you really think you can earn..."

Scott's forehead furrows.

Mr Olsen scrapes his ergonomic leather chair against the floor. "I am going to show you something." He speaks in a hushed, conspiratorial tone. "Now I don't want this to go further than these four walls, understood?"

"Yes, Sir."

Mr Olsen scrutinises Scott's expression, as though unsure whether he can be trusted. Eventually, he shuffles through his drawer and passes Scott a payslip. His glasses jangle on their chain against his cashmere jumper as he leans towards the boy. "I earn forty-seven thousand pounds a year, Simon, and..."

"Scott."

"Scott. That's a hell of a lot of money, and around double the average salary. Do you understand what I'm saying?"

"Er, yes, Sir." Scott sits very still in his chair, noticing for the first time just how sad Olsen's eyes look. Buscemi, thinks Scott. Bingo. Steve Buscemi would play Olsen in the movie adaptation of his life.

Olsen makes his voice lighter and smiles, revealing nicotine-stained teeth. "So you want to work in the film industry? Why not work at your local supermarket in the DVD section? Or a local Blockbuster? They often hire straight out of school. It wouldn't even matter what marks you got."

Scott rubs at the side of his temple. The room suddenly feels completely airless.

"You never know," continues Olsen, oblivious to the effect his words are having. "One day you could be manager or even regional manager." He slams his desk drawer closed. It makes a satisfying thud. Case closed. "OK, settled. Now get back to your lesson. I'll get some contact details of the local supermarkets and get them to you, Simon." Mr Olsen swivels back to his computer. Places are limited on the "Inspiring Ambition" seminar up in Gleneagles in June, and he wants to make sure he submits his form in time. The golf up there is second to none, and he has a new 9-iron he's desperate to try out. He looks through his bifocals and squints at the screen.

"Yes, Sir." Scott realises with terror that this is the point where he is expected to simply stand up and walk out of the door. But in the five minutes he's been in the office, Scott's legs have mutated, the bones melted down, his body a cast filled with blood spiralling towards an unseen vortex. He holds onto the chair arms and takes his time standing up. Scott is viewing the world through 3D glasses. The door, that previously was only two feet away, has taken on an Alice-in-Wonderland perspective, dangling off its hinges, its shape multiplied, jagged and overlapping. He moves slowly towards it, his head reeling.

Mr Olsen raps his knuckles on the table. "Excellent," he says without looking up. "Now let me get back to work."

Like a disorientated diver suffering from the bends, Scott is desperate for air. Thinking is a struggle. His chest hurts. The corridors become distorted, longer than Kubrick's in 'The Shining' and Scott reaches the end sooner than he'd expected, his feet pivoting automatically to take him down the stairs. He steps aside without realising to let people past, feeling the breath of every one of them on his face.

Colours bleed like warnings into his peripheral vision: the neon green of an emergency exit sign, making a mockery of linear thought. Later, at home, he'll try to articulate it. He'll compare the experience to the cat-and-mouse ride he'd been on as a kid at the end of the pier. A rickety wooden roller coaster that crept you up to the top. Individual carts clanking and creaking all the way and you could see the top. You could feel the sea spray and, if you leaned back, you could see the waves below. You began to feel scared for what was to come, but excited too because there it was, the top in sight. And then, you reached the top and you could see a bend, a curve to the left. Only the cart wasn't turning with the tracks, it was going forward, straight on and on and it should be turning and you were sure this was the end. You looked into the horizon and checked the metal bar across your waist. Maybe you prayed, you couldn't remember afterwards. And then the cart would jolt. Left. Suddenly. And the sea would disappear and you wouldn't even notice the drop because you were still getting over the fact you'd nearly died. And you climbed out of the cart at the bottom, shaky legged, and pretended to your parents that it was no big deal.

He staggers his way through the school's warren of corridors until he finds a fire door. He pushes it open into sunlight and runs.

Sid karate chops the air violently, unaware of how ridiculous he looks, flailing his arms around until the wasp finally concedes and hums away from him towards the tennis court. It feels like a well-earned victory. The little bastard had been bugging him for the best part of an hour.

On days like this, Sid doesn't mind sports lessons. He squints towards the action on the other side of the playing field. Lucy

Rogan has just hit a home run, to her surprise and that of everyone around her. Nigel Ball is barking orders at Babbage, who is scurrying around in the undergrowth trying to retrieve the ball. The girls are circling Lucy, hi-fiving and hugging. Sid swipes at a long blade of grass. He bets she smells like Juicy Fruit. Once or twice a year, it happens that the indoor pitch is double-booked and, instead of the girls playing netball and the boys five-a-side, the PE teacher drags them all into the sunlight to play rounders together. For the rest of the lesson, it's two hours of flirting and sizing each other up. For Sid, it's an excuse to catch up on revision. He volunteers himself as deep fielder, standing too-far out to have to catch any hits. He pulls his revision notes from his tracksuit.

"Psst."

Sid hears the noise just as a stone lands on the grass in front of him. He looks up from his notes.

"Psst." The voice sounds again.

Sid turns around.

Scott is hunkered down in the overgrown grass at the edge of the field, like an army recruit on unchartered territory. He's dressed in khaki combat trousers and a two-tone baseball top. Sid can see his grin from here.

"Er, hi," whispers Sid. "I thought you'd gone home."

"I did," says Scott. "Wanna get out of this place?"

Sid glances across the field. There are still twenty girls lined up to bat. The match is nowhere near over. "I can't," he says.

Scott checks the big G-Shock watch on his wrist. "You caught one half an hour ago," he says to Sid. "That buys you some time."

"What, you've just been sitting in the bushes? Watching?"

Scott kicks at the grass. "Come on mate, let's get out of here." He stands up and walks across to Sid, no longer playing. Scott had thought he could manage alone today but, truth is, he feels bad for snapping at Sid earlier. He needs the company of his only friend.

Suddenly, a cheer rises from the other side of the field. Sid thinks, thinks again, says, "What the hell," and follows Scott's lead.

Nobody notices as the two boys jog towards the small lane that leads away from school grounds and towards freedom. In fact, no one will notice that Sid has gone until Lucy Rogan hits another home run in the final five minutes, and nobody is there to catch her out.

"Do you smoke?" asks Scott. Sid's clothes always reek of the stuff, but the habit seems at odds with this perfectionist of a lad, who refuses to lie on the grass for fear of getting his clothes dirty.

"Nah. No way. Why?" asks Sid, taking a seat on a bench instead.

"No reason." The city rolls out ahead of them. In the afternoon sun, church spires and lead roofs unfold along the horizon like pages of a pop-up book.

"Do you?" asks Sid, wondering which way his house is from here. The stillness, the smell of cut grass, being so far above the city, removed from normality, it's like Sid imagines a holiday would be like.

Scott shakes his head.

"I thought you'd be the weed type," confesses Sid. "No offence but you seem a little…" His voice trails off. He's still unsure of his boundaries around Scott. Friendship is a new concept to him, and he feels certain already that it's a constant game of tug-of-war. And Scott seems a little volatile. The last thing Sid wants is to upset him again, land on his arse.

"Fuck that, it messes with your head." Scott pauses, grins and looks honestly at Sid. "I don't need any more help with that."

Sid nods. He thinks he understands. He's never considered himself a sad person. He's never known anything other than his small, self-contained world. Though he can't wait to go to university he knows that he'll always be tethered to his mum. He's resigned himself to that. Despite his lack of friends, Sid's always been, well, alright considering. Maybe it's something that oozes from the walls of the house he's grown up in, a kind of inherited stoicism, stiff upper lip and all that, which means that Sid just gets on with things. Scott's different. Scott fights against demons that no one can even see. Just watching the back of his head, Sid can tell that Scott is tense. The way he holds himself. His mind is always elsewhere.

"So, you know this morning. You should probably have come back to class. What did Olsen say to you?" Sid is genuinely curious. He'd waited for Scott at lunchtime. Something really bad must have happened, to make him jump ship like that.

Scott stands up abruptly and wipes the dust from the seat of trousers. "Fuck Olsen," he spits. "Hey." He pulls a bottle of Lucozade from his satchel. "I got you something."

"Thanks." Sid studies the bottle intently.

"I love these bottles. Reminds me of one of those Shaolin monks."

Sid stares at Scott, clueless.

"You know, like Hare Krishnas but with those wicked kicks." He watches as Sid takes a swig. "Wanna watch 'Terminator 2' at my place later? I've got the deleted scenes version."

"You've got what?" asks Sid, struggling to keep up.

Scott taps out a rhythm on the bench. "You know the Dali Lama was once asked what surprises him most about mankind."

"You know you're a little...different," says Sid, smiling between sips. He could get used to this.

"So are you."

They take turns kicking the empty Lucozade bottle along the main road. The blonde hairs on Scott's arms have bleached even lighter in the sun and for the first time in months, his sunglasses are necessary. Sid's cheekbones are scorched from sitting out in the sun. He'll have a new batch of freckles tomorrow.

"So why have you been to so many schools then?" asks Sid, chipping the bottle up in an attempt at a trick.

Scott stumbles a little. "I'm disruptive, I'm a dreamer and I'm a nuisance. That's according to my last three teachers anyway." He takes a run up and slams hard at the bottle.

"How? You don't seem disruptive to me," replies Sid.

"I'm not. Well I don't mean to be." He pauses. "Why can't you be great? Why can't you earn loads of money?"

Sid looks at him carefully.

Scott continues. He takes his rubber ball out of his pocket, passes it quickly from hand to hand. "What's the difference between me and Spielberg, me and Schwarzenegger? You know people laugh when I even compare myself to them." He stops, addresses Sid. "I mean, why can't *I* do what I wanna do? Why can't *I* be great?"

Sid clams up. He wishes he had an answer for his friend. Scott seems upset by the conversation. He's doing that thing again, where he scratches the side of his head as though trying to get to the workings of his brain. Sid's never really thought about comparing himself to anyone else. Him and Spielberg, well, they exist in different universes, as far as he's concerned. And he doubts that Arnie's ever had to clean up his mother's vomit. "Hey," he remembers suddenly. "What time is it?" He checks his watch and panics. "I've gotta go."

"Hang on, I thought you were coming to my house? To watch..."

Sid gets his bearings, picks up his pace. He still has time. "I will," he promises. "Just can't tonight."

"Well I'm not going home yet anyway." Scott wants to avoid his mum for as long as possible. "I'll walk you home."

"Sure, whatever," says Sid, his mind already elsewhere.

CHAPTER 5

The black Mercedes is parked nose to tail with an identical silver one, the way only cars in movies do, driver-seat to driver-seat. Ambling along behind Sid, Scott notices the cars straight away. They strike him as completely at odds with the neighbourhood, which is like something out of a magazine feature on post-war panoramas. It's as though the town planners forgot to lay tarmac here. Like a forgotten corner of Gotham City that the Bat-signal never illuminates. The bare ground is pot-holed to oblivion, deep gullies filled with rainwater although it's been dry all week. Scott scribbles some thoughts on the back of his hand. This new part of the city is a revelation to him. It's a film location scout's dream.

The back street has opened unexpectedly onto a desolate sixties shopping parade; a small, low concrete building with a walkway through the middle. By rights, the two cars should have their windows smashed out, or keys scratched along their pristine bodywork, at least. Cars like that in a place like this can only mean one thing. Undercover cops.

Scott has been following his friend's sparrow-boned gait in silence for the past half an hour. He's not sure that Sid's even aware that he's being followed. Sid is propelled by a private sense of purpose and his steps are even quicker than usual. He seems at home in the carnage.

Scott hesitates out of sight and surveys the scene. He can imagine that, once, this row of shops would have been the hub of a community. The faded signs above boarded-up windows proclaim, "Quality Meats", "Famous Pies", "Fresh Bread", "Keys Cut While U Wait". Scott can't imagine anything being produced here now. He navigates the potholes and tries to keep his wits about him as he follows Sid across the empty concourse. Ahead of them is the closest thing to a shop that could exist here. A broken neon sign above the door reads "Nanda's No. 1 for Convenience." Sid is heading straight for it.

Scott hasn't always been a wanderer. It's a habit that arrived along with adolescence. Nightmares that had been occasional and manageable when he was a kid became pervasive, and stopped limiting themselves to the night. For a while he'd tried to communicate with his foster parents, but there was never a good time to tell them that he feared his head was falling apart. Instead, he developed coping strategies. There was the music, of course. And then came the wandering. Often, when he can't sleep, he'll set off walking, a kind of somnambulistic half-sleep journey, not thinking about the route and not noticing the darkness. Hours later he'll kind of snap out of it, find himself miles from home and turn back. Somehow, his mind will have subconsciously picked up on monuments and signals, and he always finds his way home before sunrise. His parents, safe in the cocoon of their king-sized bed and black-out curtains, remain none the wiser. Nothing really scares him anymore.

He glances into the driver's seat as he passes the black Mercedes. His instincts were right. No one other than a police officer on a stake-out would sit in a car with closed windows on a day as sweltering as today. The man looks the same age as Malcolm, wearing crumpled plain clothes and steel-capped boots that mean business. The interior of the car looks to Scott like a ready-made film prop, an homage to detectives everywhere: a wooden beaded seat rest; empty takeaway coffee cups scattered next to the man's feet and a pair of binoculars on the passenger seat. In the brief moment of eye contact between him and the policeman, Scott recognises the familiar weariness of a fellow insomniac. He smiles weakly. The sound of 'Hotel California' drifts from a tinny radio in the car as the detective holds the boy's gaze. Feeling the weight of the man's quarter century of professional distrust, Scott kicks a stone and looks away.

By the time Sid spots his friend's reflection in the smashed mirror outside Nanda's, and realises that Scott is still following him, it's too late to turn back. Fuck, he thinks. Scott had been so uncharacteristically quiet that he'd thought he'd lost him. Thought his mate had got bored and wandered off, had second thoughts and realised that Sid was too dull to hang around with after all. He can't buy the vodka while Scott is around. He'd have to explain everything. Shit. *Shit.* This is too close for comfort. Sid nervously places his hand on the cracked pane of glass in the shop door and takes a deep breath. He can't do this. He needs his boundaries. He grits his teeth and pushes open the door.

"Alright," Sid mutters at Mr Nanda as he begins to stalk his way slowly around the edge of the shop.

Mr Nanda looks up from his newspaper, surprised by the boy's hello.

"Did you see Starsky and Hutch back there?" Scott jokes loudly, bundling in clumsily behind his friend, tripping over the extension cable that Sid has subconsciously learnt to step over. "Oh, hi, mister," he says to Mr Nanda.

Ignoring Scott's running commentary, Sid traces his fingers along the shelves, hoping that his face suggests he is looking for something specific. He inspects an out-of-date tin of custard powder and places it back on the shelf.

Scott looks around at the shop, amused by the novelty of such a ramshackle set-up. From a back room, out of sight, he can hear the audience cheers of a daytime reality show. He evaluates the shelf in front of him and smiles. In pride of place is a stack of the multi-coloured ink pens, identical to the one Sid gave him this morning. The price on the tag is 20p. That figures, thinks Scott. He looks around for Sid. They could be here all day. Sid seems confused, both at ease and completely freaked out by the shop. Scott sighs and opens the lid on a chest-high freezer. After the heat of the day, the icy blast is a welcome respite and Scott is happy to stay there until Sid finally finds what he is looking for.

Mr Nanda eyes the blonde boy with curiosity.

Looking down at the bright blue ice-pops buried under frost at the bottom of the freezer, Scott is perturbed. Something about the colour reminds him of his dream last night. It was all blue filters and unnatural light. He blinks hard. Not for the first time, Scott wonders whether films are to blame for his nightmares. It's true, films fuel the vividness, so that his dreams are now almost always tinged with a Lynch-esque light, and there is always an element of the grotesque. Maybe that's it. Maybe his mum is right. Maybe he should just stop watching films. He smiles at the thought, sticks his head deeper into the ice.

When he re-emerges, the shopkeeper is standing beside him. "Can I help you, my friend?"

Scott grabs the first thing he sees, an imitation Snickers bar. He grins at the man. "Just this, thanks."

Mr Nanda smiles back at Scott with something like relief.

He has his fair share of weirdos in this place. He's just glad that the vodka boy has a friend. "See you again," Mr Nanda chirps as Sid holds the door open for Scott to leave.

"They didn't have what I was looking for," Sid blurts out quickly as they stand on the concourse outside the shop.

Scott opens the bar of chocolate and tears it in half. He hands the biggest piece to Sid.

Sid shakes his head and kicks at the dirt. "Ta, though."

"I can't believe places like that still exist," laughs Scott, cramming the sub-standard chocolate into his mouth. He screws up his face. "Where do they find this stuff?"

"He's a good guy, Nanda," snaps Sid. He makes a decision, feeling bad about it, but not being able to see any other way out. He's running out of time. "Better go!" he declares without warning.

Scott frowns as Sid slaps him firmly on the back. It seems out of character, unusually cheery.

"See you tomorrow, buddy," says Sid, already walking away.

"OK. Bye." Scott watches his friend disappear around the back of the building. Beyond the shops, the field slopes down across wasteland towards the two-up-two-down doll-house terraces that look barely fit for human habitation. So *that's* where he lives. Scott re-traces his steps towards the alleyway. As he does, he notices that the police cars have moved. It's just the black one now, and the driver's expression is serious. He's looking at Scott with the same suspicion that so many other adults flash his way. Fuck him, thinks Scott. So much for the insomniac solidarity. He heads towards the large houses in the distance, one foot in front of the other, trying hard not to dwell on the policeman's look, and the feeling of panic for his friend that is beginning to settle in the pit of his stomach.

He walks a little faster. Recently he'd read about flaneurs, urban wanderers, the idea that walking can redeem the soul. He's willing to try anything.

Detective Russell holds the binoculars up to his eyes and squints. They'd almost had him. The skinny boy had looked nervous, scampering away out of sight a little too quickly for Russell's liking. As for the blonde boy, he had trouble written all over his face. Young men like him, with a fearless stare and nothing to lose, were the reason the detective carried a handgun.

He adjusts the beads behind his seat. Therapeutic my arse, he thinks. Although it's what, two years since she walked out, his life is still full of relics from his ex-wife, and even his police car bears the evidence of her attempts to normalise him. The pine air-freshener that dangles from the rear-view mirror will never sanitise the things he's seen in his fifteen years at the head of his racket. People think of York as a tourist town. All they see is the bloody Viking museum, the quaint shopping streets, the Minster and the prize-winning gardens. But Russell knows better than anyone: scratch at the surface and the worms will come crawling. He takes a slurp of cold coffee. The way those two boys were acting, it's put doubts in his mind. Maybe this case is more than they think. Maybes it's worse than bootleg alcohol. Maybe it's drugs or people trafficking, he wonders, hopefully. Russell pulls his thumb over his forehead, trying to smooth out his migraine. Christ, he hates summer.

"Aye, aye," he says, slouching low in his seat. He holds the binoculars to his eyes. The skinny kid is creeping back into view, walking along the perimeter of the building, checking there's no one around. Through the tint of the lens, the boy looks even paler than usual. The city is full of people like him, ghost kids, resilient as cockroaches. Russell feels not the slightest sympathy. He'd had it tough growing up himself. Newcastle in the seventies was no time to be a wimp. "Go on," urges Russell aloud to himself, as he watches the boy walk into the shop. "There's a good lad." He reaches for his radio and calls in for back-up.

"Where's your friend?" Mr Nanda's chest sinks visibly as the young lad re-enters the store.

"I don't have time for friends," replies Sid, rummaging in his bag for his wallet. Today has gone on too long. All he wants is to be home, for all the crap he knows he'll face there. He just wants to be with his mum. Today's empty bottle clinks against his keys.

"Not so fast," warns Mr Nanda. He gestures towards a school kid at the other end of the store. The kid is flicking through the out-of-date comics, laughing out loud. Though Nanda's voice is warm, his eyes carry a serious warning that Sid heeds. He pushes the empty bottle deeper into his bag and waits for the all-clear.

Outside, the silver Mercedes creeps through the backstreet. Detective Russell's tired voice crackles through the radio static. "Come on, you little bastard. We've nearly got you."

Mr Nanda drapes a fatherly arm around Sid's shoulders. "Come, come." He ushers Sid towards the back room, where the theme tune to 'Neighbours' is playing at full blast.

"No, no no, NO!" Detective Russell slams his binoculars down against the dashboard. The little bugger is almost out of view. This won't do. He hasn't sweated his balls off in the car all day just to miss the moment of actual purchase. Russell disentangles himself from the mess of his car and runs towards the store.

"My brother owes your mother a book," says Mr Nanda loudly, steering Sid past the kid and the comics.

"What?" Sid isn't in the mood for distractions. "A book?"

"Yes." Mr Nanda pulls aside a curtain. "Go on. Through to the back."

Sid finds himself in the alley behind the shop, face to face with a man unloading boxes from a car. "Hello?" he ventures quietly, unsure how to address the man with his back to him.

Omar Nanda spins around. "Sidney?" He places the box on the pavement. In his mid-forties and spritely from decades of five-a-side football, Omar Nanda usually has a permanent smile. He looks Sid up and down. "Sidney, we're concerned."

Sid angers slightly, feeling vulnerable. He begins to look for an escape route, his breathing turning to panic.

"Your mum," continues Omar. "She needs help, not this stuff." He points to a crate of unlabelled bottles, identical to the one Sid has in his school bag.

Sid stands his ground. Now he remembers. The kid in his class, Reashan, he said something about his dad owning a shop. The man in front of Sid is wearing a Liverpool football shirt, same as the one that Reashan wears every day under his school shirt. Reashan and his dad have the same dimples. Sid explains his position. "I have to get it from you. You don't..." Sid pauses. "You don't judge us."

"But it's been seven years. When you first came in here, you couldn't even see over the counter." Omar studies the boy's face and is appalled by the things some parents will inflict on their children. Childhood is supposed to be a time for playing, for doing all the shit you want to do, before it's too late. "Have you spoken to a doctor?"

"I've got the money."

"Your mum. I remember her from before, from when we were teenagers. She used to be so…" Omar struggles to think of the right word for the wild beauty he used to see down The Anchor on a Friday night. Back in the day, Karen had been the kind of girl you would drop everything for. All dancing eyes and inimitable cool. "She used to be so *alive*. What about a social worker?"

Sid fumbles with his glasses. "You're the one that sells it! Why do you care? Long as you get the money, right?" He points at the bottles. "Just give me one," he insists, slamming his coins on the roof of the car.

Detective Russell keeps his eye on the sliver of light coming from the alleyway as he engages Mr Nanda Senior in small talk at the front of the shop, all the time edging backwards towards where the boy went. Holding one conversation while eavesdropping on another has become something of his trademark, and Russell listens with interest as the conversation in the alley heats up. Surreptitiously, he gives the signal to his supporting officers, to be ready to make the move.

"I'll give it you on one condition," says Omar.

Sid stares at him, waiting. Increasingly he feels as though his whole life is conditional. One more won't hurt.

"You will come with me to the social services. You'll tell them what's going on."

Sid considers the proposal. In the beginning, when his mum first sent him out to get her booze, there were suspicious stares. Sid had developed a whole arsenal of lies: his mum was working late, it was a family celebration, it was a one-off...and he had spent months as an eight-year-old, traipsing around the city, making sure never to go into the same shop twice. Then he had overheard someone talking about Nanda's, and he'd been going there since. That was the thing about Nanda's. He stopped having to lie. They didn't judge. Or so he thought. Usually Sid prides himself on being honest, but today he seems to be breaking every rule in his own book. Spending money he didn't have on a gift for a friend, skipping school... one more lie won't hurt. "OK." He smiles. "I'll come with you tomorrow after school. I need to go home now though. Just give me it." He pauses. "Did you really used to know my mum?"

Omar hands a bottle of vodka to Sid, who buries it quickly in his bag and turns to leave.

Detective Russell seizes his opportunity. He barges clumsily into the alley and wrenches Omar's hands behind his back. "Omar Nanda. You are under arrest for supplying illegal alcohol, supplying alcohol to a minor, distributing illegal alcohol." He cuffs the man. This part of the job never ceases to give him a bit of a hard-on. "Oh, the list goes on."

Omar writhes his body away from Sid, forcing Russell to move with him. With their backs turned, Omar manages to gesture at Sid. "Run," he mouths.

Survival instinct kicks in and Sid's body suddenly remembers how to run. Clutching his bag close to him, he sprints away, squeezing through a hole in the brick wall just as three other police officers stumble onto the scene.

"Find him," bellows Detective Russell. "He's evidence."

Sid only looks back once. The police officers are miles behind. Used to stomping the city pavements, they are out of their depth, flailing on the uneven terrain, three unfit figures silhouetted against the pink evening sky.

Sid runs at full pelt, stopping only when he reaches his back gate. He bolts it shut behind him, hastily lets himself into his house and double locks the kitchen door. Slumping down onto the floor, he watches his chest heaving up and down. Every sense in his body is heightened. He can't believe he made it.

"Sidney?" Karen's voice wails from upstairs. "Sid, is that you?"

The kitchen reeks of vomit, and Sid is afraid to look in the sink, knowing what he will find. It's becoming a habit of hers these days. He drags himself up from the floor and composes himself. "I'll be right up," he shouts.

Scott keeps his head down, sensing that his mum is waiting for an apology that he isn't willing to give. The meal she's cooked for them is the usual mid-week mashed potatoes and lamb cutlets, but Scott can tell by the way his meat is a little burnt around the edges that she's still pissed off with him. That's the one good thing about his dad being home, Scott thinks: his mum ups her game in the kitchen, making the most of the new gadgets that Malcolm has brought home from his travels and trying out gourmet recipes in an effort to impress him. Scott pushes the lumpy mashed potato around his plate with his fork.

He spent most of his walk home trying to fathom out Sid. Something had spooked him at the store. Sometimes Scott wondered whether Sid wanted to exist at all. There seemed to be something always holding him back. Sid was a reluctant talker, but it was getting to the point where Scott wanted to ask. The rounders game had summed up his friend: Sid seemed to think he could go through life on the sidelines, waiting for someone to throw him a catch.

He draws the mash up into a column and surveys his work. The surrounding green beans act as a perpendicular wall. The carefully-balanced cutlets meet in the middle, creating a formidable arch. Scott pours gravy around the base to form a pseudo moat.

"Stop it!" Elaine's fork clatters onto her plate.

"But look," Scott protests. "Dinner becomes a fort, a Viking fort."

Elaine begins to hack her lamb into increasingly smaller pieces. "For heaven's sake." She chews at the meat. Why can't they just sit down to a normal meal, like everyone else in this street. "Just eat it, Scott, there are millions starving..."

"...I'm gonna eat it." Scott flattens the construction with his knife, in one fell swoop. "I'm just mucking around. It's a kind of..." He looks across the oak dining table at his mum and stops. He reaches for the salt. "Mum, the salt shakers everywhere always have dints in them. How come?"

Elaine slams her cutlery on her plate again. Jesus Christ, here we go again, she thinks, her patience finally at its end. "This is what they are talking about." She wrenches the salt shaker out of Scott's hand. "You can't just eat your bloody dinner like a normal kid. You have to bugger about with it like a bloody two-year-old!" Her hands are shaking, the pearly manicure that she had done for her husband catching the light. Lately, she's been fighting the feeling, that sentiment that no mother should ever admit: she wishes that things had been different. That Scott had been different. That he'd gone to a family who knew how to handle him. That they'd chosen a different kid instead, one easier to love. She speaks quietly, her bottom lip beginning to tremble. "I've taken the time to cook it for you..."

"Mum. I'm going to eat it." He picks up his cutlery and begins to eat. "I'm not doing you any harm."

Elaine watches her son. Even the way he eats grates with her. She's done her best with him. God knows she's tried over the years, but he has these... *habits*. He makes her cringe. She can't keep it in tonight. She doesn't want to. "You're so bloody annoying!".

Scott stops, his feelings hurt. He didn't ask her to watch him eat. He would happily trade it all in for solitude. He doesn't need her company. He doesn't need anyone. Sometimes he wonders if she sees him as a pet: something to stop the house feeling empty - something to feed. A way not to be alone in a too-big house and a loveless marriage.

Elaine can see it in her son's eyes. The hatred under the surface and the complete lack of respect. The *judgement*. She scrapes her chair suddenly against the flagstones.

Scott flinches at the noise. Anger is usually his dad's domain. She's over-reacting, he knows that, but he's gone too far this time, he can tell that too. He should have just stayed out.

"I've lost my appetite now, thank you!" Elaine scrapes her plate furiously and clatters it into the dishwasher.

"Sorry." Scott means it. His mum suddenly looks so frail. Even dressed in her power suit, still wearing her heels, her shoulders are rounded and her satin blouse looks ten sizes too big. She is defeated.

She grabs some kitchen roll from the dispenser and speaks without turning around, her nails gripping the edge of the granite. "Are you also sorry for sending your dad off in a bad mood this morning? He's off for five weeks now, and that's the last I saw him."

"Just the five?" retorts Scott sarcastically. He raises some green beans to his mouth.

Elaine whips around suddenly, her face mottled with tears. "Scott!" she screams. "I can't deal with you! You're unbearable. This thing with your dad."

It scares Scott to see his mum so worked up. That year when it was just the two of them, after his dad left the first time, he learnt that they weren't that dissimilar, Scott and Elaine. They both have their struggles. He just wants it to stop. He wants it all to fucking stop. "There's no thing," he says. "He just doesn't like me."

"Nobody does, Scott! You've no friends, your dad can't fathom you, you drive me round the bloody bend! Even your teachers, who get paid to deal with you, can't bloody well handle you!"

Scott chews, trying to ignore the lump in his throat, feigning nonchalance. It's true. Every word she says is true. What does she expect him to say?

She almost doesn't say it. Elaine's throat is hoarse from shouting. For all that people think of her as uptight and highly strung - and she knows what people say about her behind her back in the office - it's rare that she ever actually raises her voice. But he has to know. He can't carry on like this and neither can she. She has to say it. "And then you're up with your bloody dreams, pissing the bed."

Scott can't take anymore. He slowly rests his cutlery together on his unfinished plate, pushes his chair away from the table and leaves.

"You're a bloody disaster," Elaine shouts after him, as Scott drags his feet towards the blue TV light flickering in his bedroom.

CHAPTER 6

With a birds-eye view of the playground and everyone who enters it, Scott finds it easy to daydream up here. He's been zoning out, sat up on the high brick wall since six in the morning so that, by now, he feels part of the set, equidistant between the ground and the overcast sky. He swings his legs against the wall and tilts back his head. He's listening to Bach on repeat. It has kept his mind in check, stopped him from thinking about the fact that he'd listened to his mum sob herself to sleep last night, while Scott had stared at the ceiling and struggled to hold back his own tears. To Scott, there was something immeasurably sad about relatives either side of a paper-thin wall, with no way to bridge the gap between them. That this person who had once considered Scott her salvation, her stab at a family (and vice versa) has so thoroughly rejected him. He blames Malcolm for that.

In the case of his father, it is never a case of "out of sight, out of mind". Even in Malcolm's absence, the house swells with his influence, both emotional and financial. The control he holds over Elaine is evident by the fact that she no longer goes out after seven, lest she miss a call from her husband, and the frantic all-day clean that occurs in the run-up to Malcolm's return from overseas.

Scott swipes a finger over the shiny, blue MiniDisc player resting on the wall beside him, a present from his dad's latest visit to Japan. The lettering is raised like braille. Scott is grateful for the gifts. For a while he had convinced himself that they were an indication of Malcolm's love, but lately he's realised they're just a way to appease the guilt. Gifts mean nothing. All this *stuff* and they still can't hold a civil conversation.

Without Scott's permission, his imagination propels him into the future, as it is prone to do. A studio audience this time, and Scott is answering questions from the floor. A man has just asked him if Sid was the first person he ever trusted. The chat show host is flashing a too-eager grin at him, hanging onto Scott's every word. Even in the daydream, Scott despises sycophantism. That's another good thing about Sid. There's none of the drapery of modern culture, none of the bullshit. It's as though Sid has stepped out straight from the fifties, uninfluenced by adverts, unencumbered by consumerism. Sid looked at Lucozade like it was a bottle of moon juice.

Back in real life, Scott turns up the music, hoping to stave off people's voices with cellos, and keeps his eye on the side entrance of the main building, anxious to see the slight, stooped figure of his friend. The detective from yesterday had invaded Scott's fitful sleep: a twelve-foot demon in his nightmare, chasing Sid through a tunnel made of shattering glass. Scott's worried for his friend.

"Hey, Sid." Scott takes out his earplugs and makes a quick assessment. Sid is uncharacteristically late. The skin beneath his eyes is dark. His shirt collar is a little skewed. Scott states the obvious. "You look tired." He sits on the bottom step of a staircase, not ready to face the academic world just yet.

"Maths first thing," Sid says. Mr Fell is notoriously intolerant of latecomers. Sid still remembers the lesson in first year, when the maths teacher made them all stand on their chairs and face the back wall, for the entire hour, just because Lucy Rogan was five minutes late. A life lesson, he'd called it. Sid had considered it a lesson in sublime entrances: Lucy had looked immaculate that day, with a new haircut and killer nails. It was then that he'd realised he never stood a chance with her, and resigned himself to worshipping from afar. He sits down with Scott anyway.

Scott persists, wanting Sid to trust him, to confide in him. "You look pretty rough. You ill?"

"No," says Sid, sheepishly. "Just didn't sleep. We better get a move on," he says as the bell rings.

A slight boy walks past them. The red of his Liverpool football top bleeds through his white school shirt. Sid catches his eye. "Reashan! Leila!"

Reashan turns to Sid. "Gori bastard," he spits and Sid looks down, ashamed.

Leila looks equally pissed off, her glare adding weight to her brother's words.

Scott pulls up his legs so they don't trip. When Reashan and Leila are out of sight, he turns to Sid. "What's gori bastard mean?"

"Dunno. Didn't sound good though, did it."

"No. Who is he?" asks Scott, incredulous that such a mild-mannered person could attract the hatred that Sid does.

"His dad owns the corner shop."

"Oh." Scott laughs. "Needs to work on his marketing skills."

Sid is quick to defend Omar. "No, he's a good guy."

Scott tries to make it clear that he's here, listening, that whatever is going on he can help with it. "Yeah but he seems upset…"

"Forget it." Sid is still blushing. He wants to keep a safe distance between his new friend and his latest enemy. He couldn't know for sure what had happened to the Nandas after he'd fled the shop, but he had a pretty good idea. The venom in Reashan's voice had suggested that his dad might have spent a night in a cell.

Scott opens the door for Sid. "Wanna go to another world?"

Sid frowns. "Eh?"

"Music," says Scott. "Keep up. Music. You like music?"

"Yeah," answers Sid quickly. "I mean, yeah." He tries to remember the name of the song he'd heard on the radio last night. It was a mix of classical and pop, a loop that he'd got caught up in. It had stuck with him long into the night. "Don't listen to much, though."

"What? It's awesome," exclaims Scott. "You need this." He pulls his MiniDisc player from his pocket and hands it to Sid. "Here. I'm done with it."

Sid stops in his tracks. A younger pupil barges into him, mutters something that neither of them catch. Scott flashes the youngster a cautionary look, but Sid doesn't notice. He's used to being pushed around. Sid turns the device over in his hands.

"It doesn't come out until next year over here," explains Scott.

Sid's jaw drops. "And you're giving it to me?"

"Yeah, sure." Scott mounts the stairs two at a time. "Check out Yo-Yo Ma," he shouts down to Sid. "Prelude No. 2."

Sid wraps the MiniDisc player in his handkerchief and places it carefully in the inside pocket of his blazer. "Thanks." He bounds up the stairs after Scott. "Thanks, mate. That's awesome."

Mr Fell is permanently out of breath. His dark shirt is the worst choice for the final summer term, when he will always be remembered as the unkempt mess of a maths teacher with permanent sweat patches under his chubby arms. He scribes out numbers and symbols on the board and turns to the class with a smug, self-satisfied air. "Go on then," he challenges them.

Sid tightens his face as he looks at the board. He'd tried to lose himself in revision last night, but his mind kept returning to the chase home, the certainty he felt that all this was only the beginning, that his life was about to change forever. He could feel himself losing control and it scared the hell out of him. He focuses hard on the equation.

Mr Fell is well aware of the hand reaching for the ceiling in his peripheral vision. It's like a goddamn fly that he can't swat. "Not you," he shouts, pointing at the class genius without even having to look. "Give someone else a go." The girl lowers her hand. That's the problem these days, kids confuse having a good memory for actual intelligence. The same girl, he'd heard, had held up her hand in a history class recently and asked his colleague, in absolute earnestness, "Did all this *actually* happen?" Like he said, intelligence couldn't be taught. Discipline, though, that was another matter. Mr Fell focuses his attention on the new boy. The blonde kid has the kind of unfortunate face that makes him look like he's always up to something. Right now, he is certainly *not* interested in the question at hand.

Scott focuses on the Shakespeare quote on his desk. It seems an eternity since he scribbled that on his first day. He can feel Mr Fell's eyes boring holes into the top of his head. Please, he begs silently. Please not me.

Mr Fell waddles up to Scott and taps his head with a piece of chalk. "Come on then, genius," he says.

Scott raises his head slowly and looks across at Sid.

"What?" mouths Sid, genuinely concerned. Scott's eyes are wide with fear, and he is eyeing up the walk to the board as though he's destined for a public execution.

"Come on," says Mr Fell. "Let's see if we can succeed where four other schools have failed."

Scott stares at the numbers on the board.

"Well, you can start to break it down, can't you?" Mr Fell folds his arms across his chest, impatient. He pulls Scott up by his coat collar.

The numbers squirm across the blackboard, white chalk maggots writhing in an open wound. Scott's hands begin to tremble.

Sid watches with growing horror as Scott drops the chalk and stares at the floor as though it's his limb that has fallen. The class laughs.

Swiping up the chalk, Scott turns again to the board. For a second, it seems that he's got it under control. He's frowning at the equation as though he might know where to begin. Then he drops the chalk again, and it's not just his hands that are trembling.

Sid hears a long, low groan of agony. It's only when Mr Fell turns to him and asks if he's alright, that Sid realises the noise is coming from his own body. He clutches at his stomach and wonders how far he should take this. Sitting there with the eyes of the whole class on him, Sid is only aware of one voice. Scott's face looms over him.

"What you doing?" Scott mouths to his friend.

"I'm poorly." Sid groans again.

"You're what?"

"I'm ill," Sid hisses.

Scott hands the chalk to Mr Fell. "I knew something was up with him, Sir. I knew he was ill."

Sid closes his eyes and lets his head fall onto the desk with a satisfying thump. He smiles as he allows Scott to take his weight, feels his body being hauled away somewhere.

In the sick bay, Sid squints open one eye and steals a look at Scott. His friend is sitting on a blue chair beside the first aid bed, holding his head in his hands. He is still out of breath from helping Sid up two flights of stairs. Scott sees him looking.

"You're alright," he says, a grin spreading across his flushed face. Scott is relieved. His friend had been out cold.

Sid raises himself into a sitting position. "I'm absolutely fine." He pulls his tortoiseshell comb from his pocket and sweeps his hair into place. "Are *you* OK?"

"I knew you were ill," says Scott, proud to have been so perceptive. "I asked you, didn't I."

Sid leans closer to his friend and smirks. "I'm not ill," he whispers.

"What?"

"I faked it," confesses Sid, still proud of his performance.

Scott tries to make sense of it. "What for? Why would you..."

"So you didn't have to do the problem at the front. You looked terrified."

Scott absorbs the confession like a bullet. He gets to his feet, not yet able to make eye contact with Sid. "You saved me," he realises out loud.

"You're my mate," says Sid glibly, as though it was nothing. Sid sits up straight in the bed and turns to face his friend. "You looked so scared. I had to do something."

"I can't believe it." Scott finally faces Sid. Both of their cheeks are crimson. "That was so kind of you."

"You gave me a monkey dusk!"

"MiniDisc."

"Yeah, MiniDisc."

Scott smiles. "No one's ever done anything like that for me before."

Sid laughs, excitedly. There'd been a certain thrill to being centre of attention, just for five minutes, on his own terms. If someone had told him before the act, that he had to make a scene in front of everyone, he'd have insisted it couldn't be done, that it wasn't in his nature, but when it came down to it, he hadn't thought twice. Sid had always considered himself a measured person. It made him wonder what other impulses were lying dormant. Terrifying and electrifying in equal measures. "I can't believe I did it either."

Scott thinks for a second. "You should be an..."

"Why were you so scared?" Sid stares at Scott, suddenly serious, waiting for an answer. His eyes follow his friend as Scott stands up abruptly and paces across the room.

Scott sits down slowly on a chair in the corner, trying to decide whether he should take a risk. The numbers thing. It had been a while since he'd had to explain that one. Aged ten and the new kid at Wynchburgh Primary, he'd run away and hidden in the woods for the day rather than have to face a maths test. They'd got Social Services involved on that occasion. His dad had been called home from Russia. "Why are they always blue?" Scott wonders.

"Eh?" asks Sid. "What?"

"Furniture in medical places." Scott scratches at the blonde stubble peppering his chin. "I just can't read the numbers."

"What numbers, it's a chair."

"On the board," clarifies Scott. "I just can't. It's not that I don't try."

"You can't read numbers?"

"Numbers, letters. If you can write it down, it can dance across the page for me."

Sid props himself higher up in the bed. The cushion behind his back is old foam, pointless in a faded jade pillowcase. Sid tries to straighten out the creases. He thinks about Scott's handwriting. The spidery scrawls skittering across a page. No wonder he can't keep his head straight. "I don't get it."

Scott sighs, then starts again, eager to say the right words in the right order. He's scared of coming across as a loser; worse, still, that Sid will *pity* him. But now that he's begun, he wants Sid to know his entire life story, the good and the unsayable. His words tumble out into the sterility of the room.

"Sometimes I can read, sometimes I can't, sometimes I can make sense of numbers, other times like this morning, it's like... I don't know, it's like a brick wall... I just." Scott struggles with the next word, a word not usually in his vocabulary. "Can't."

A pause, as Sid digests the rant. "That's weird," he says, finally, not knowing how else to put it. The word feels like an insult as soon as it leaves his mouth.

Scott is unperturbed, on a roll now. "I get bad dreams as well."

"Like what?" asks Sid.

"Like..." Scott scratches at the blue leatherette seat. There is a hole in the surface and Scott wonders whether it was already there. "Like I'm normal, I'm an old man in a nursing home."

"An old man?"

The door squeaks open and the school nurse enters. She is just out of college. Under any other circumstances, the boys might have looked twice. "Hiya," she says, brightly. "Sid?"

Sid nods. She turns to Scott.

"You can go back to your lesson, thank you." The nurse has already perfected the perfunctory but cheery tone of voice necessary for her profession.

"Can he stay, Miss?" pleads Sid.

The nurse looks briefly at the blonde boy. He seems to be sitting deep in thought, as though she interrupted him. She's not sure she wants him in the room. He's too distracting. She doesn't want to encourage their relationship. She's pretty sure this kid is the same one she saw on the street the other day, holding his head in his hands with his headphones on, dancing alone like he was on drugs. "No," she insists. "Off you go."

Scott gives Sid a high five before he leaves. "See you later." He stops at the door. "D'ya think I'm like James Bond, Miss?"

The nurse rolls her eyes. "No."

"That's a shame," smirks Scott. "You could have been my Bond Girl." He smiles as he closes the door. He's damned if he's going back to Mr Fell's class. He has his own answers, and he's a feeling he might now have someone to share them with.

Sid shuffles in the comfort of the luxury bean bag and presses fiercely on the Gameboy buttons, his lips pressed in silent concentration. The corner comes up quicker than he'd anticipated, and he throws his whole body into it. The car crumples against the wall of the race-track and the screen pixelates into darkness. Sid can't hide his disappointment.

"You'll get the hang of it," assures Scott. He is lying down on his bed, bouncing his rubber ball against his bedroom wall. He takes a break to hand another can of Coke to Sid, then begins again the rhythmic throw and catch. There is a giant world map poster tacked to the wall, and Scott is aiming at a different country with each throw.

"All this stuff and you're playing with a ball." Sid gently places the Gameboy on the beanbag, unaware of how much the console costs but fully certain that he cannot afford to replace it. He holds the can away from his body and fizzes it open.

"The ball helps me think," explains Scott.

"What you thinking?" asks Sid. In his own room, in his natural habitat, Scott makes sense. His shambolic way of dressing and lack of co-ordination is not out of the ordinary here. In this enormous room in this enormous house, Scott has free reign to create his own sanctuary, and Sid is mesmerised by the collection of objects that make up Scott's den. Every available surface is covered. Books litter the floor, their spines bent. Nothing is straight. It seems a room for a thousand hobbies: sports equipment, musical instruments and gadgets sit unused in boxes with foreign language instructions. In the corner of the room two guitars lean against the wall, their necks in a quiet embrace. Sid eyes up the acoustic and wonders whether he can have a go. He reckons that's the kind of guitar his dad must have had, that used to live in the case under his bed: polished wood and a folky pattern. "How did you get all this stuff, anyway?" He twangs at a guitar string and immediately silences it. "You must be loaded."

"My dad is," answers Scott, leaning back on the bed with his hands behind his head. He cups the bouncy ball in the palm of his hand. "My thoughts can be too intense, too fast. The ball slows everything down."

Sid takes a swig from his can. "I wish I could get more stuff."

"You can," replies Scott, as if it was obvious. "Just work for it."

"Doing what?"

"All sorts. Paper rounds, jobs around the house. I sold gerbils last summer." Scott mis-throws the ball and it bounces away.

"What do you mean?" Sid is intrigued.

Scott jumps up off the bed. "It's simple. I want..." He rifles through the top drawer of his desk and pulls out a MiniDisc player like the one wrapped carefully in an old T-shirt in Sid's bag. Sometimes, in his enthusiasm for spending, Malcolm forgets what he's bought his son and Scott ends up with duplicates. He tosses it aside, pulls out a fork instead. He holds it to the light. "This Robert Welch fork. I just think it's beautiful." Scott continues. "I see what it costs, whatever, and then I go get jobs to pay for it."

"Job for your parents?" Sid had seen the family portrait in the kitchen. Scott's parents looked nice, normal, *together*.

"Sometimes." Scott closes the drawer. "I save the money and buy it. Like I said, simple."

"Wow." Sid is blown away by the simple mechanics of work.

It strikes him as a fairly straightforward formula, but he knows he would never have the guts to put himself out there like that. He wouldn't know where to begin. "I wish I could…"

"You can," says Scott, not allowing Sid to take his default position. Sid suffers from a crippling inferiority complex. He has this idea, that annoys the hell out of Scott, that he, Sid Sadowskyj, is inferior to everyone else. That the rules that apply to the rest of the world will always pass him by. Sometimes Sid acts like he's a Victorian worker, chained to the mills. This is the twenty first century. The world is small when your dreams are big. Scotland to Sydney in less than a day. "You can," Scott repeats.

Sid looks dubious.

"Of course you can. Can you tie our own shoelaces?"

"Yeah?"

"If you had to earn ten pounds tomorrow, could you?"

"Yeah, I guess?"

"But what if I said a thousand pounds or ten thousand?"

"Well, no!"

"Why not?" Scott is bouncing the ball faster now, alternating target between Doc Brown's hair and Sigourney's eyes. "We're told we can't and we don't believe we can, so we end up not doing it. Vicious cycle." He stops bouncing and turns to Sid. "Let's do it!"

Sid twangs at the guitar again. "Do what?"

"Go make ten thousand pounds!"

Sid hears the car tyres scrunching along the gravel into the driveway. Scott misses a beat and bounces harder.

"We can't just do that," exclaims Sid. With the imminent arrival of Scott's parents in the house, Sid feels sure that they should stop the conversation, resume normal service, start talking about school or something instead. Maybe he should leave.

Scott gawps at him. "Haven't you heard anything I just said?

Of course we can."

Sid frowns. "We're different, you and me. Some people are born great..." he mutters.

"What?" Scott stares at Sid for a second.

"Nowt." Sid is looking around the room for his jacket. He was sure he'd placed it carefully on the back of Scott's desk chair, and he is angry to find it on a heap in the carpet. Downstairs, the front door slams shut and Sid hears high heels on the marble floor.

Scott finally stops bouncing the ball. "It's a pattern. We are born, enter a system. Teachers and parents pile on influences and we all respond and out pops mild-mannered DVD clerk Simon Smith. Why do we earn twenty k a year if we're lucky? Why work nine til five? Why two weeks in Spain?"

Sid has lost him again. "Who's Simon?" He dusts down his jacket with the palm of his hand.

"Simon, Scott, Sid, whatever. Don't you see, we're all inter-changeable to them." Scott frowns. Sid doesn't seem to be hearing him. He collapses onto the bed. These are the thoughts that consume most of his waking seconds, and most of the seconds he should be sleeping too. He's never had to actually articulate them before. It's exhausting. "Life is your own, Sid. You don't have to be a passenger. Have a look around. Don't be led. Don't be normal."

"Normal." Sid slouches on the bed beside Scott. "What is it with you and that word?"

Scott sighs. "I'm just saying, you can do what you want. Start your own business. We could start something together. Fly fucking fighter jets. Anything."

The afternoon sun casts its shadows down the wall. Sid hears Scott's mum preparing dinner downstairs. He contemplates the image of himself as a businessman. The sharp suit. The fast car. The private jet. The freedom. "Like what's his name," he says.

"Richard Branston?"

Scott begins to bounce the wall again. The noises from downstairs get louder. Elaine is noisily clanging copper pots on the spotless Aga. "Pretty sure it's Branson."

"The pickle guy?"

"No, the billionaire," snaps Scott. "I can only eat that without the lumps."

"Never had it." Sid sits still on the bed, his jacket folded neatly in his lap. He can sense that he's outstayed his welcome. Scott seems annoyed, and Sid can't be bothered to figure out why. Good smells are beginning to waft up from the kitchen, and Sid can't help but feel a little jealous. "Wish I was a billionaire," he says with a wry smile. "We're always broke."

"But your dad must do alright?" Scott studies his friend's face. "What exactly does he do again? You were a bit vague yesterday." He's pushing it. It's cruel. He can tell Sid doesn't want to talk about home. But he's annoyed at his habit of avoiding the subject. It's not fair. Scott's dealt all his cards on the table.

"Anyway," says Sid, acutely aware of Scott's anticipation. He pushes himself off the bed, finishes his drink and looks around for the rubbish bin.

Scott gestures to leave the can anywhere. "What? You off then?"

"School's finished." He rests the can precariously on the edge of the desk. "If I'm late home my mum will worry."

Scott picks up the ball again and lies back down on his bed. Commitment, he thinks. That's all it takes. Commitment to a single, simple idea. "Close the door on your way out," he instructs Sid without turning his head.

"Bye, then," says Sid quietly.

Elaine is shocked to see the slim young man in a school uniform who appears at the bottom of the stairs without making a sound. Trousers an inch too short, white socks beneath the hems. Scott has never been the type to bring friends home. She wasn't even convinced he'd *ever* had a friend. "You scared the life out of me," she says, dropping the gingham tea towel.

"Sorry." Sid hands her the towel and shoves his hands into his pockets.

Elaine studies his face. She is relieved that Scott is capable of human interaction, but something in the boy's eyes and the cut of his clothes makes her wonder if this is the kind of lad her son should be associating with. The boy looks malnourished, and Elaine's first fear is that it might be heroin. You never know these days.

Sid scurries out of the front door, pressing his new headphones into his ears before he's over the threshold.

Elaine can hear her pasta boiling over on the hob, but she remains at the window, watching the youngster through the Venetian blinds as he checks his watch and begins to run down the street. She has no idea what to make of him.

CHAPTER 7

It's the third time Sid has listened to the concerto since leaving Scott's house and he's already beginning to feel calmer. Yo-Yo Ma. The name sounded to Sid like a kid's cartoon. He didn't expect to take it so seriously. But the music soared. It seared. Retrospectively, it seemed the perfect soundtrack to Scott's rant in the bedroom earlier. This was music to dream by. Scott had a tendency to come across as a radical, but Sid was almost sad to be out of Scott's world, the wide avenues of his affluent neighbourhood, where the music seemed to swell in rhythm with the tall trees. It made him wonder what he was missing out on.

Maybe being normal isn't all it's cracked up to be, he thinks. He turns up the volume and rolls up his shirt sleeves for the first time in his life.

Reashan feels bad for doing it. Of course he feels bad. Going after Sid, it's like hunting down a wounded pup. He's a too obvious target; the underdog in every situation. The latest rumour was that Sid had had some kind of fit in class, spaced out on the floor like a stinking mad animal with his eyes rolling back in his head.

It wasn't in Reashan's nature to cause trouble, but it wasn't as though he had a choice.

He keeps his head low as he peers out of the back window of the battered Vauxhall Astra. The Watson Brothers aren't messing around. Gavin Watson is holding Reashan's ankles so tightly that the gold ring on his middle finger sinks into the schoolboy's flesh. Nicky is in the front, keeping an eye on the pair of them.

"He's coming," says Reashan, ducking down out of sight as he views Sid turning into the alley. His classmate is listening to music, ambling along without a care in the world. Reashan thinks of his dad's broken nose and the threats that the Watsons had made on his sister, Leila. He no longer feels guilty for dobbing on Sid. Desperate times. Sid had it coming.

"You certain?" In the driver's seat, Nicky Watson pulls the peak of his baseball cap low over his forehead.

Reashan nods furiously.

Nicky springs the front seat forwards and reaches across the handbrake to open the passenger door. "Fuck off then."

Reashan hesitates for a second, surprised that it had been that easy. He rubs at his ankles as, next to him in the back seat, Nicky's older brother releases his grip and cracks his knuckles in preparation for Round Two. Reashan suddenly has a flashback to Sid in second year, getting changed next to him on sports day, the way Sid's shoulder blades stuck out as though he hadn't eaten a decent meal in months. He didn't want to think about what was about to happen.

Nicky narrows his slate grey eyes at the school-kid. "What you waiting for, a fucking medal?"

Reashan doesn't need telling again. He scrambles out of the car as quickly as he can. He's done his bit. The rest is up to Sid. He's a smart kid, thinks Reashan, as he runs towards home. Maybe he can talk them round.

Without saying a word, Nicky and Gavin open their car doors in synchrony.

The familiar alley appears too soon. Nanda's looms at the end and Sid feels sick when he sees the police-regulation corrugated iron shutters on its windows. The place is most definitely closed for business. Overhead, the clouds begin to spit.

"Jesus, you'll break him in two," says Nicky, eyeing up the teenager walking towards them.

Gavin twiddles the rings on his left hand. "Isn't that the point?"

The alley is too small for the three of them, so Sid rushes to reach the end so that the men can go on their way. But the men don't move.

Instead, the bigger one, built like a brick shit-house and with a temper you'd be a fool to fuck with, widens his stance, blocking the alley completely.

"'Scuse me," says Sid.

The man steps aside and then seems to think better of it, slamming a hand across Sid's path. His green bomber jacket scrapes against the side of the brick wall as he inflates his chest to full capacity.

Sid appeals to the bully's acquaintance. The other man is less typically macho, wearing a Harrington jacket with neat tartan lining. His grey eyes are still and lupine, with pinprick black pupils.

The man holds out his hand. "Nicky Watson. The famous Sidney Sadowskyj, I presume."

Sid turns on his heels, but he has barely put one foot in front of the other before Gavin grabs him by the collar and lifts him back. Sid's feet don't touch the ground.

"First rule." Nicky pulls a half-smoked cigarette from behind his ear and lights it with a vintage Zippo that looks suspiciously to Sid like a prize from a previous kill. The initials engraved on the silver case are not "NW". He blows a coil of smoke into Sid's face. "Never return to the scene of the crime."

Gavin tightens his grip. "Rats like this one always come crawling back."

Sid's chest feels compressed. "Think you've made a mistake," he manages to protest.

Nicky laughs, a surprisingly high-pitched giggle that stops as soon as it begins. His face is suddenly serious again. He takes a deep drag. "Do you have any idea how much money you've cost us?"

"What my little brother here's trying to say," says Gavin, his clenched fingernails drawing blood on the side of Sid's cheek, "is that you've given us a problem, you little bastard. That shop made us a lot of money. And you got 'em nicked."

Nicky stubs out his cigarette on the mossy wall. "Capiche?"

The backseat of their old car smells like violence and mould. The rain is falling all over the bonnet now, drops as big as pebbles on the windscreen. It's almost hallucinogenic. They are completely alone.

"Ten bottles." Sid closes his eyes, trying to take it all in. "How am I meant to sell ten bottles a day?"

"See that's what you're not getting," seethes Nicky through gritted teeth. "I don't care." The kid is so fucking *green*. Like he's grown up in an institution or something. "That's *your* problem now."

"But I didn't do anything."

"You got caught. You exposed my distributor to the police." Nicky draws a picture of a hangman on the window, which is steaming up quickly with the breaths of three people on edge.

"I didn't," protests Sid. "I just…"

Nicky adds the final beam to his stick-man's gallows. "I don't want to talk about this," he says. "I've given you a job to do, now do your bit. Understand?"

Sid takes a deep breath. "How much is a bottle?"

"They're four pounds each," says Gavin.

Sid finds his notebook.

"What the fuck you doing?"

"…-m-making notes."

The Watson Brothers look genuinely appalled.

Sid tries to get back on track. "They charged me five quid."

"That's the mark-up, you pillock."

"They have to make something," explains Nicky. "Otherwise where's the incentive?"

Sid thinks for a second. "So, do I get the pound this time, then?"

Nicky wipes his sleeve across the window and erases the hangman. If this kid weren't such a weakling, he could make a half-decent apprentice. He had the kind of mind you needed to succeed in business. "Shift enough bottles and we'll talk about it, Sid. Can I call you Sid?" Nicky clears his throat. "Course I can, I can call you whatever I want. You work for us now."

Sid nods weakly. "I'd better take one bottle now."

"No need," smiles Nicky. "There's a crate in your shed at home. You ought to give that shed a clean, by the way."

"What?" Sid is scared.

"Covered in bird shit," adds Gavin.

"How do you know where…?"

"There'll be another one there tomorrow, and the day after that.

Leave the money under the crate." Nicky opens the car door. "Better get to work."

Sid clambers out of the car. The shop concourse is a messy pit of brown sludge and overflowing potholes. Sid is drenched within seconds.

"Oh," says Nicky. "Almost forgot." He reaches into the back seat. "Do you want your game back?" He holds out the MiniDisc player with a smile on his face.

Sid outstretches his hand.

Nicky narrows his eyes at Sid as he drops the machine onto the ground. His red boots grind against the device until it is an indistinct pile of blue metal shards, a miniature airliner lost at sea. He smiles again at Sid. "We're not friends. Remember that."

This time of day, before Sid comes home from school, is always the longest. Between the last drops of yesterday's bottle and the first glass of today's. Karen tries to be good, to make it last but, when the shakes set in, abstinence is easier said than done. She pulls her robe close around her body and pads barefoot into her son's bedroom again. She could have sworn she heard voices in the garden.

She opens his bedroom window and lets the cigarette butt fall into the back yard below. Moving with slow, drugged movements, she is careful not to be seen by the neighbours. They're all the same around here. Nosy cows the lot of them, always have been. Karen is still embarrassed when, in moments of lucidity, she remembers how Sid persuaded her to go out in the yard in the heat last summer, the way she'd heard them all bitching about her over the back wall, felt their eyes looking at her, judging her.

Karen slumps on the floor with her back to the wall, nestling herself comfortably in the space between the bed and the bottom of the window frame. She lights another cigarette. Sidney's room never ceases to amaze her. He's always been her little soldier, organised and dependable, and his bedroom looks like a corporal's barracks. He carries so much in his mind that he doesn't need possessions. Karen scratches at the back of her hand, the skin already red raw. It's the chemicals, she thinks. She's told him not to get the cheap stuff. That he can buy her less food instead, if it comes to that. The chemicals in the cheap stuff. God knows what they put in it. It's poisoning her.

There was a time, Karen thinks hazily, when Chanel was all she used. Back then, around here, people didn't even have a name for girls like her. She'd spent a summer alone in Paris at the age of sixteen. She made her own clothes. She wore red lipstick and pink nail varnish, at the same time. She refused to settle for a local lad. The back of Karen's hand begins to bleed. Now look at her.

She un-tucks Sid's duvet, drags it off his bed and wraps it around her body, curling into a heap on the patterned carpet. Funny how, after all these years, despite all Sid's fastidious washing, the faded flowers on the duvet still smell like her mum. She closes her eyes and waits.

Karen watches her son remove his shoes and hang his wet jacket on the back of the kitchen door. He's doing it on purpose, she thinks. No urgency about his actions. He doesn't give a shit. Not really. Leaving her here to rot, day in day out. His hair is soaking, and he's swearing under his breath. The boy needs to watch his language. He doesn't even see her, sitting there on the couch, rocking back and forth, her hands wrapped around her knees. The boy needs to get his priorities straight. "You're late!" she screeches.

Sid jolts, startled into the reality of the mess in the kitchen. At some point in the day, she's tried to make a cup of tea and given up half way through the process. The cold tap is still running. Sid attacks it so tightly that his hand is sore when he walks calmly through into the living room with a clean glass and a new bottle of vodka from the stash in the shed.

Karen eyes him suspiciously. "Where have you been?"

Sid takes the smallest table from the neat nest of three and places it within easy reach of his mum. "Watch your toes," he says, pushing the table as close as he can get it. "There was a queue at the shop."

Karen spins the top off the bottle and swigs straight from it. It's down her neck in one swallow. She winces.

"Have you had anything to eat today?" asks Sid. He hadn't even had time to pick up some chips on the way home. He's starving. His mum is even paler than normal. Usually, at least her cheeks have some colour in them. He'd been terrified that the Watson Brothers had done more than just deposit the crate and leave, and he'd raced home, worried about what he'd discover. He needn't have worried. It's just the usual homely mix of accusations and anger.

Karen takes another glug. "Quite a queue that makes you an hour late."

Sid shuffles from one foot to another. "How about some pasta?"

A third swig. The bottle is half-empty already. Karen is past caring about food. What's the point? It's not like she needs all the energy she can get just to lie in bed all day.

"Slow down, mum," begs Sid. "On an empty stomach."

Karen's breath is short. She clasps the bottle with both hands and glares at her son.

Two pairs of identical, sad eyes. Sid is the first to look away.

"If you'd got home on time," she accuses, "I wouldn't *have* an empty stomach."

Sid shoulders the responsibility. She's right. It's all his fault. He should have come straight home from school, told her the truth from the start. He could have avoided all this mess, if he'd just kept his head screwed on. His mum had been warning him about "bad influences" since the day he was born. "Sorry."

Karen grimaces with each sip, her dark eyebrows articulating her sorrow. "God, it's bloody awful." She tries to smile. "I'll be glad when I've had enough."

"Just sip it mum. Will you." Sid notices the sore patch on the back of her hand and his heart sinks. "Please... please mum."

With the kitchen door closed Sid almost manages to forget what is happening in the living room. He can tell from the occasional clink of the glass bottle, that she is still in there, but he reckons he has half an hour to himself before the vodka kicks in to full effect.

Sid is happy to have something to focus on. He adores the precision of cooking. The choreography and the magic of a series of simple movements correctly orchestrated to provide something of sustenance. He flicks on the kettle. Next, he places a saucepan on the hob and adjusts the handle so that it is parallel to the front of the unit. He pours pasta quills into the pan, removes two, looks again at the size of the portion and replaces one. Then he hears it. His mum has re-tuned the radio and she is humming along to a song she doesn't know. Five minutes, he re-calculates, as he pulls a block of stale cheddar from the fridge. She's obviously been drinking even faster than he'd feared. He frowns and waits for her grand entrance.

Karen knows this song. She *knows* this one. This is the one with the video, with the girls in the car and the pink hair. A wide grin spreads across her face. Just for a minute with songs like this, Karen is beautiful again. Back in The Anchor with a crowd of admirers and eyes only for one man, the dark, brooding foreigner playing backing guitar.

Lucasz Sadowskyj. Love of her life. Bane of her fucking existence. She finishes the bottle and turns up the music.

Sid senses his mum in the kitchen before she speaks. He concentrates on the cooking.

"I'm sorry."

"It's fine." He deftly stirs the pan with one hand while taking his mum's hand in his other.

"Come on, darling." Karen entwines her fingers with Sid's. "Let's dance."

"Look, I'm not doing that, I'm cooking." He lowers the heat to a simmer anyway, knowing he doesn't really have a choice.

Karen is already dancing, marking out patterns with her bare toes on the old lino tiles. "Come on, you boring sod! It's party time. Come and dance with Mummy!" Her untied hair tumbles onto her shoulders in dark waves.

Sid glances at the clock. Two songs and the pasta will be ready. He gives himself up willingly, glad to see her happy for the first time in months. Dancing *does* something to her, ignites memories in a way that being surrounded by all this stuff can't do.

Karen tugs at her son's glasses. "Take them off," she says, and Sid wrestles gently to keep them on. "You're getting to be handsome," she says. "Just like your dad."

Sid winces slightly at the comparison. He wonders if that's why, subconsciously, he chose the thickest glasses on the rack. He didn't want the pressure of reminding Karen of the man who left her. He never wanted to look like anyone but himself. His mum persists, and Sid takes off his glasses and rests them on the counter. Half-blind, he can lose himself in the dance, something that doesn't come naturally.

She holds him tight, transformed, and they look happy, like two kids at the disco who found each other for the last song.

"Why do you let me do it?" moans Karen, wiping her hand angrily across her mouth. The bile dribbles down the side of the toilet, missing the bowl completely. "You should have told me to stop."

Sid tenderly strokes her hair away. Her forehead is burning. "I did, mum." With the other hand, he runs her flannel under the cold tap and squeezes it out. This part of the dance always leaves him reeling. It's inevitable, choreographed with the same precision as the rest. He manoeuvres himself around his mum in the tiny bathroom, balances everything they need on the narrow glass shelf. Two toothbrushes. One tube of value-brand toothpaste that barely has a hint of mint. One bar of cheap white soap. The bathroom suite, as old as his nanna's collection of china, is the same luminous yellow as the stuff that'd come out of Sid's throat on the only night in his life that he had been drunk. Cider in the park. He thought it was what you did as a teenager. Thirteen years old and he wanted to see what all the fuss was about. He was puking acid spew for the next two days, his head over the toilet like his mum is now. Sid had learnt his lesson. The truth is, he doesn't trust anyone enough to get drunk in their presence. He'd want to know that he'd be looked after, regardless of how fucking hard it might be. He just wants to know that someone would care if he overdosed and, right now, looking on as his mum disappears into a different level of consciousness, he's not convinced that anyone would even notice.

The terraced house is finally quiet. *Dear Sir,* writes Sid. His pen hovers above the paper and he realises that every single muscle in his body is tense. He doesn't care. He thinks about the phrase, that his mum had sweetly whispered into his ear as they waltzed through the kitchen earlier that evening - "blood runs thicker than water, son" - and he feels choked with responsibility. He wants to open up his veins and see what really runs, how deep all this bullshit really goes. He crosses his legs on the bed and wishes he still had the MiniDisc player. He tries to remember the cellos, desperate to hear a sound that matches the thunder rumbling through the chambers of his heart. He hasn't felt this angry in a long time.

I wish you could see her like this. See what she's made of me. Nights of a million emotions and all I want is a dinner with more than two ingredients and to watch some crap programme on the telly. To do my homework without the soundtrack of wretching. To not have to worry about the mess she's making, the mess she has made. The mess she's made of me. The normal stuff, that everyone else takes for granted. I want the fridge bulging with fresh food and the fat white cherub that sits beside the front door of Scott's house, the mum that can button up her shirt straight, who can stomach her food, the dancing that doesn't mean doom.

He is writing quickly now, the marks on the page heavy with anger as he notices a speck of blood at the corner of his duvet cover.

I have so many questions to ask you. People think I'm too quiet and I want to scream at them. Sometimes, I think if I didn't stay quiet I would never shut up. I would instantly become one of those weirdos I avoid in the street - the muttering, stuttering freaks with their inappropriate clothes and speech impediments. It's safer not to say a word.

He hears a groan from Karen's bedroom and considers going in to see her. He takes the paper from his knees, pauses, thinks better of it and continues to write. *Fuck it,* he scrawls, his writing almost illegible. He scribbles angrily over the profanity and takes a deep breath. Outside his window, the clouds darken to a deep indigo. He wonders what Scott is doing tonight, can't help but feel jealous at the apparent ease with which his friend can switch off. Sid resigns himself to the fact that he will always be an outsider. He thinks carefully about the events of the past few days, the actions that set in motion the cyclone that's swirling around him, threatening to annihilate his universe. He can't get it out of his head, the certainty that Scott is both his saviour *and* the one who will ruin him. Saint and sinner. The sensible student in Sid reminds him that exams are approaching, to keep his head down until autumn comes and he can cut loose and start over, one way or the other. The other half of his brain, the one now buzzing with music and stories and what if questions, urges Sid to hold on to Scott as though his life depends on it. He writes a word in neat capitals on the page. *TRUST.*

CHAPTER 8

Scott jumps down from the school wall as Sid approaches. They pick up their conversation seamlessly, as though twelve hours of home life had never occurred.

"You know what we were talking about yesterday," begins Sid, already nervous. Without the bottle of vodka in his bag, he feels lighter than usual, unarmed. It's a deceptive lightness: far from having vanished, his load, his secret - the stash - has just moved closer to home.

"The fighter jets thing?" asks Scott.

Sid looks confused. "No, the money. Making money. Going for it."

Scott stares intently at his friend. "Yeah! We can give it a go now if you want."

Sid wants to, and the devil on his shoulder urges him to skip school, retrace his steps and see what happens. He restrains himself, as usual. "I can't miss school again, though. Once was bad enough." He doesn't know what he's afraid of. It's not like his mum will ever find out. Even if Olsen came knocking on the door looking for him, Karen wouldn't answer. But he feels like he owes it to her, not just to finish school but to excel at it. Karen gave up all her plans when she had Sid. University, a place on a nursing course, *life*. It seems like the least he can do. He can sense that Scott is about to try to persuade him otherwise. "I'm not missing school," Sid insists.

"School's for wimps." Scott can't hide his frustration. He'd thought yesterday was a breakthrough, albeit a minor one. He'd invited Sid into his world for starters. He'd never done that before. It had felt like stage one in his quest to bring Sid around to his way of thinking, make him see that the real enemy is conformity. Sid had been blinkered for far too long. "So you wanna earn some money, right?"

Sid's thoughts are suddenly interrupted. They've reached the school auditorium. Reashan and his sister are sitting in the empty hall, two chairs turned together in the back corner. Reashan has his head in his hands. "Er, Scott," he says, catching Leila's eye. Just give me a minute."

Scott excuses himself as his friend dives in.

With an eye on the door, Sid sits down. He keeps his voice low, stuttering with fear at the memory of last night. If he's to conquer The Watsons, he needs an ally. Reashan and Leila kept themselves to themselves. They seemed like reasonable people. "These two men came to see me... about the shop."

Reashan scowls at Sid, his teeth gritted, incredulous at his nerve. The scrawny little fuck really expects them to help him out?

"You're on your own," says Leila. "My dad and uncle, they're in real trouble. We've had to close the shop. We don't have any money. They're talking about moving down south, having to start over again."

"I'm sorry." Sid feels exposed again, as though the whole school is watching. "I didn't mean to get you into any trouble," he says gently.

"Come on." Reashan hasn't got time for this. They were meant to be sitting somewhere quiet, making a plan to save their family, not chatting with the enemy.

"Look, Reashan, please, I'm...."

"...Whatever," says Leila, waving her hand dismissively, getting up to leave.

Sid strides back towards Scott, a new-found purpose directing his step. "You ready or what?"

"What was all that about?" asks Scott.

"Nothing." Sid weighs up the pros and cons of starting something with Scott. Something proper, a means of making ends meet, somehow tunnelling a hole out of this mess and coming out alive. I wanna do it." He scans the corridors quickly to check there are no teachers nearby and slams his hands against the fire escape.

"Now you're talking." Scott takes hold of Sid's bag, wanting to lighten his load. To his surprise, Sid lets him carry it.

"How much you wanna earn?" asks Scott.

"We," clarifies Sid without hesitation. "It only works if we're equal partners."

Scott is impressed. "Why don't we become partners in business?"

"Yeah." Sid smiles. "That's what I'm saying."

The chess board is set up mid-game on an ornate side table, the wood so highly polished that Sid can see his reflection in it. He picks up a chess piece, surprised at the weight of it. "Who's winning?" he asks.

Scott rummages in the door of his eight-foot fridge and emerges with a bottle of orange juice. He fills two tumblers with ice from the dispenser on the front, hands a glass to Sid, casts his eye over the chess pieces and takes a long gulp of juice. "It's a bit of a stalemate." He bites hard on the ice, giving himself a head freeze.

"Your mum's not in, is she?" asks Sid. He's not keen to bump into Mrs Elliott again.

Scott shakes his head. "Out at work. I always come home in the daytime." He looks again at the chessboard. It was Malcolm who'd taught Scott to play. The *know your enemy* thing, it was all part of his dad's paranoia, a constant need for one-upmanship that Malcolm was intent on passing down to his son. Fuck it, thinks Scott. He'll play by his own rules from now on. He tries to imagine what his dad is doing now. An eight hour time difference. Scott reckons that Malcolm's sitting in some casino, under a seedy artificial strip-light, a girl on each arm. He'll have paid them to be there. He makes Scott sick.

"Whoa," shouts Sid, casting a protective arm over the chess board.

Scott is suddenly snatching at the pieces, tossing them one by one over his shoulder.

"Aren't you in the middle of a game?" asks Sid, reaching under the leather sofa for a knight.

"It's fine, leave it." says Scott. "We haven't played in months." There is a sadness to his voice. He clears his throat. "The game's over."

"Who's we?"

"Me and Malcolm."

"Who's Malcolm?" asks Sid, wondering if Scott has a brother.

"Foster dad."

Sid is surprised. "You call him by his first name?"

"Sometimes." Scott folds the chess board into itself. "He's more of a Malcolm than a dad. You know?"

Sid nods, realising that it's the same in his house. Karen is more of a Karen than a mum. She'd never been able to hide her real self behind the label, like most people's mums seemed to manage.

"Don't let people hide behind their roles," cautions Scott, reading Sid's mind, his voice regaining its focus.

Sid fills the silence with a stroll around Scott's living room. Scott had closed the heavy curtains as soon as they walked in the door,

111

and the room feels ever more grand in the half-darkness. A Steinway piano, immaculate and dust free, catches a glimmer of light in the corner of the room.

Scott sees him looking. One nil to Malcolm. Mission accomplished. The piano was certainly a "talking point". "It's Malcolm's," says Scott.

"Does he play?" Sid resists the urge to lift the lid and run a finger down the ivories. He's never played a piano before. Wonders if he has it in his genes.

Scott shakes his head. "I don't think that's the point of it."

Sid knows better than to ask more questions. Scott watches him carefully as he shuffles around the room, looking at photographs and ornaments, the prizes of his parents' life together. It looks quite convincing from an outsider's perspective. Sid stops at the drinks cabinet. The globe has always fascinated Scott: a wide sphere that opens to reveal a secret stash of party booze.

Sid lifts up a bottle. "Does your mum like vodka, too?" he asks.

"What?" asks Scott. Sid is holding up a £200 bottle of brandy. Why would Elaine drink vodka? Vodka is for drunks. Everyone knows that.

Sid replaces the bottle swiftly.

"You hungry?" asks Scott.

They set up base camp at the kitchen table. Sid pulls a notebook and two pens from his bag, Scott grabs a box of Pop Tarts from his. He places a foil wrapper on Sid's knee. "Strawberry," he says. "Sugar and jam," he adds, sensing Sid's apprehension. "I think."

Sid takes a cautious bite, approves, takes another. "So," he says. "Eighty pounds a day." Eighty quid, split down the middle. Forty each and farewell to The Watsons. "Forty pounds each. Anything we make on top of that is a bonus." Sid takes another small bite out of his Pop Tart.

Scott turns to face him, puzzled. "It's all bonus, isn't it?" He studies Sid's expression. For the first time since they met, Sid's face looks open. Scott isn't sure whether it's trust or desperation. He's afraid to ask. Sid had come around awfully quickly to Scott's way of thinking, and Scott's curiosity is getting the better of him. He makes his question sound casual, incidental. "What do you want the money for?"

Sid thinks carefully. "Need not want. Is it achievable?"

"We can do anything," affirms Scott. "It's just about joining the dots, you know, find the right product or service for the market."

Sid is already out of his depth. "We have to go down the market? Can't we just..."

Scott interrupts. "To get what you want from life, you have to hack it."

"You think about this a lot."

"I do," admits Scott. "Life hacking."

Sid tries out the new phrase on his tongue. "Life hacking." He likes the sound of it.

"You can apply it to anything," explains Scott. "Even family."

Sid glances quickly at Scott. He wonders how much he knows. For some reason, Sid always has the impression that Scott knows far more than he lets on. He always seems five steps ahead, his mind working overtime. Sid feels like a fool. He wishes he'd never lied about his dad working away. It's playing on his mind. The chess game. All that stuff about knowing your enemy. Sid was beginning to get the impression that Scott's dad was far from a loving presence. He blurts out the next sentence without really thinking about it. "Do you ever just wish he would die?"

Scott knows exactly what he's talking about. He looks Sid straight in the eyes. "I dunno, sometimes." As soon as he says it, he visualises it: Malcolm's body laid out on a marble slab, the room

113

heavy with the kind of time-melting quiet that only a dead soul can cause. Scott flinches, but only a little. He back-tracks, more out of guilt than a genuine change of heart. "Nah... just... that he'd have an accident or something... a lobotomy... wake up to what an absolute prick he is." He frowns deeply. "Not die though. Not really. If it wasn't for Malcolm and Elaine, God knows where I'd be."

Sid laughs nervously. "Sorry, I dunno why I said that."

"Thought I was meant to be the morbid one," says Scott, smiling.

Sid smiles too, happy at the implication that they are already irrevocably joined, that they are beginning to find their roles, that he, Sid Sadowskyj, might have something unique to offer. From now on in, anything seems possible. "So," he gets back on track. "How are we gonna make our millions?" He unfolds the local newspaper from his bag.

"Where'd you get that?" It's not like Sid to carry anything superfluous.

"Your doormat. You don't mind, do you?"

"Nah mate, go right ahead. You better read anyway."

Sid furrows his brow and holds the newspaper close to his eyes.

"Do those glasses even work?" asks Scott.

"They're kinda old," admits Sid. He slowly moves the newspaper further away, until the text becomes clear. "It's fine, there's just a bit of a knack to it."

Scott tries not to laugh.

Sid reads from the small print. "Dog walking?" He looks up.

"No way. I'm scared of dogs."

"I didn't think you were scared of anything."

Scott shows Sid a deep scar on his wrist, from a dog attack years ago.

Well that clears up that one, thinks Sid. He'd wondered what the scar was from. He continues to read. "We've got mechanics, hairdressing, gardening, lost dogs, loads of lost dogs. More handymen. Colon cleansing." He looks up again. "What's colon cleansing?"

"My mum had it done." Scott pulls a face. "It's where they clean your back door out."

"Your back door?" Sid's baffled. "What about your front door?"

Scott smiles. "Not sure. We could do that." He gets an image he could do without. "Cleaning, I mean. People hate cleaning."

"Have you done it before?"

Scott shakes his head furiously. He jumps to his feet, offering himself as evidence. His school shirt is covered in stains. The hems of his trousers are caked in mud. There is green ink on his face, from yesterday. "How hard can it be? We just clean it til it's clean."

Sid thinks for a second. "Cleaning is fine. It's just a question of creating order. It's kinda therapeutic, actually." He hesitates. "That's what my mum tells me, anyway. But nah, that's not it. It's gotta be more specialist than that. Something that nobody in here is doing, like... a unique selling point."

"We've gotta have something to give us an edge."

"Exactly, yeah. What do people hate to clean?"

"Toilets," suggests Scott.

"Yeah but only the public ones and that's different. Cars?" suggests Sid.

"Eh? What's not to love there. Outside. Water fights. Nah."

Sid thinks again. "Dogs?"

"Would you quit with the dogs? No dogs." He snarls his own canine teeth, making Sid laugh. "Shoes?"

Now Sid is aghast. "How lazy do you have to be not to clean your own shoes?" He checks his trainers. Immaculate. He thinks hard. "I once saw this programme, right, where this old man went to people's houses and asked them stuff about their house and their jobs... and it was really boring but I remember one thing sticking out and it was that everyone hated doing their ovens. Cleaning their ovens." Sid can practically feel the lightbulb blazing above his head. "That's what we've gotta do. We've gotta clean ovens."

"Boom!" shouts Scott. "We'll do it five quid a go."

"Twenty," interrupts Sid. "Twenty pounds."

"Easy peasy." Scott is impressed.

Sid does a quick calculation. "That way, we only need to do four a day, two each."

"You're right," says Scott, his face animated. "We don't want to undersell ourselves."

"If we spend about thirty minutes per oven, plus a little travel time in between. I reckon we can start about three after school."

"No, no, no," says Scott. "We go all day. Make more money that way."

Sid stammers a little. "We can't go all day, Scott. I've gotta go to school, I've gotta get an education. I... I can't miss school again. I don't mind today but..."

Scott can't believe he has to go through this again. "You don't need to go to school. School is... it's a..."

"A social construct designed to impede our independence and stilt our inherent desire for curiosity," parrots Sid, looking kindly at Scott to show he's not taking the piss. "I get that. I do. But it's my final term. It'll give me options for university. I've got responsibilities."

"What responsibilities?" quizzes Scott, his tone slightly aggressive.

Sid can't answer.

"Well *I* don't need to go. I don't need some dissatisfied bully trying to tell me stuff. I've got all the options in the world. Doing *this* is one option." Scott lowers his voice. "I mean, do you wanna earn your forty quid?"

"Yeah," Sid concedes. There's no getting around it. "OK, yeah."

Scott opens the cupboard under the sink. That's the good thing about his mum. There's never any rummaging around wondering where she might have put something. Everything has its place. And the oven-cleaner belongs in the bottom cupboard, next to the white trainer-polish. "There we go."

Sid smiles. "Boom."

CHAPTER 9

"What is it?" asks Sid, puzzled by the blue console Scott has thrust into his hand. He steps out of the shadows of the preened buddleia bush, finds himself covered in feathery purple petals. He dusts himself off.

"I know" replies Scott. "It's just a 3310, nothing special. It's kinda old now. But I had two, so..." he holds up an identical object. "My number's in there already."

Sid is embarrassed to ask how it works. Since their house phone was disconnected years ago, he's become used to the old-fashioned method of simply making an arrangement and *sticking* to it. Being where you're meant to be at the agreed time. Facing the consequences when you screw up, come home too late. Mobile phones suggest to Sid an off-the-grid existence that is at once terrifying and seductive. "Thanks," he mutters and, following Scott's lead, tucks the device out of sight in his top pocket. "Shall we start with these houses?" He gestures to the detached mansions around them.

Scott frowns. "No way."

"But they're massive. Everyone will have money to spend."

Scott laughs out loud at Sid's naivety. "Big house don't mean big heart."

"Alright, I just thought..."

"We'll start on your street," chirps Scott. "More houses, higher probability of success." He turns left towards the part of town that he's seen Sid retreat to.

Sid freezes. "I don't think that's a very good idea," he snaps.

"Why not?" asks Scott. He's glad he's stayed in his school uniform. Like the religious guys who knock on his mum's door selling badly-drawn magazines, he thinks that maybe the uniform might give him kudos.

Sid uses the time to think of a plausible excuse. "My mum's working from home today," he lies. "Her desk is by the front window. Besides," he elaborates, "she knows everyone on the street, so she's bound to find out somehow. She'll kill me if she finds out I'm skipping school."

Scott takes Sid's explanation at face value and sketches in more details to the image he's building up of Sid's mum. He imagines a well-dressed woman who talks with her hands like a character out of a Woody Allen film. Who keeps her house immaculate and irons her son's clothes every night without fail. Who manages to hold down an incredible career in the creative industry as well as going to yoga classes once a week, making smoothies for breakfast and watching her son like a hawk. Mr Sadowskyj is still a cameo role in Scott's imagination, a hazy figure lurking in the background. Scott wonders what the deal is. "Fair enough," he says. "How about that street up by the park? The one shaped like a horseshoe."

"Deal," says Sid, glad to have got away with it. "I just, er, can't get my uniform mucky."

Sid takes a penny out of his pocket. "Heads, you go first."

"Fuck that," says Scott, the gravel giving way under his boots as he strides up the driveway.

Sid follows reluctantly behind him. "You sure your dad won't mind me wearing his suit?" he shouts, the tuxedo tails catching on the rose bush by the front gate. Ten steps later and he is walking straight into Scott, who's stopped to ask a crucial question.

"What we going to say?"

"I dunno." Sid hadn't considered that either. "What shall we say?"

"Erm." Scott thinks. "We clean ovens?"

"That's too brief," says Sid, getting into the role. "We need something more professional. I know. You knock and I'll say, 'Hello ma'am, we're in the area offering a four... *five* star oven cleaning service. Would you like your oven cleaned?'"

Scott raises an eyebrow. "Where'd that come from? You don't talk and next minute you're Tony Robbins?"

"It's different isn't it, it's acting. Who's Tony Robbins?"

Scott can't resist these opportunities to take advantage of Sid's naivety. "Ah," he jokes, "he lives at twenty-three."

"Oh," says Sid.

"Right, come on." Scott rests his boots on the pristine doormat and knocks on the stained-glass window.

"*Three* knocks, Scott," cautions Sid behind him.

"Ooh, buzzer," notices Scott, pressing it to be sure.

"No." Sid waits for the door to open.

The man who comes to the door manages a "What?"

"We do," begins Sid. "...ovens," he finishes, as the door slams in their faces.

"What happened to Mr Personality?" laughs Scott.

There are certain houses that kids always avoid on Hallowe'en and that door-to-door salesmen don't bother with. No. 1 Orchard Drive is one of those houses. A seventies bungalow set back from the road, with a miniature mock-Versailles fountain in the driveway.

Above the front door is a homemade sign that warns, *Never mind the dog - beware of the owner.* CCTV cameras cover every angle of entry. The house screams "Stay Away."

"Do we have to?" asks Sid, holding back.

"At some point, yeah. Let's get it over and done with."

Inside the porch, a Betterware catalogue has been placed carefully beside the empty milk bottles. On its front cover, a yellow post-it note contains the message written in capital letters, "Once again, no need for your tat. Thank you all the same."

"Well, they clearly have too much time on their hands. Could be a good sign." Scott knocks enthusiastically.

They stand side by side. After an eternity, a shape appears behind the glass. They nudge each other as seven locks are rattled and opened, one at a time. Sid braces himself. Scott feels surprisingly relaxed. He's actually kind of enjoying himself. He's ready to prove his point to Sid, buy some new films with the money he earns and take it from there.

The man who answers has a face that suggests he's spent his whole life in a state of perpetual disappointment. "Yes?" He doesn't speak so much as exhale the word. He can barely be bothered to look at them.

Scott and Sid back away from the door.

"Hello," chirps Sid. He'd read a sales website that suggested he should kill them with kindness. Everyone loves a trier. That kind of shit. He smiles his best smile.

The man sighs long enough for Sid to nudge Scott as if to say *I warned you.* The man clasps his arms behind his back.

"We just wanted to ask," Sid begins.

"I know very well what you just wanted to ask. You little buggers come round here every week." He uncrosses his arms and pops his knuckles loudly.

121

Scott winces. There are two versions of old age that terrify him. The first is rotting away in a nursing home. The second is aggressive seclusion, hating everyone and everything, building a fort around your own insecurities. Scott likes to think he has enough strength of character to avoid such a state of mind, no matter how loudly his demons may scream.

The man continues. "*Mister*, can I have my ball back? *Mister*, my stupid parents sent me to ask whether you could spare a pound to sponsor me for my pathetic sponsored egg and bloody spoon race. *Mister*, did you know that there are starving Africans in the world and would you like to do something about that?"

Sid stares at the man. He has cut himself shaving and there is a blob of white tissue stuck to his upper lip. It disturbs Sid. Not just the lack of care, but that he should open the door without sorting himself out a bit first. Life isn't about appearances, he knows that better than most, but they definitely count for something. Out there in the world, you should present the finest version of yourself. Even if you only have a tenner a week to work with. The man is yelling now. Sid's heart is racing, and Scott is wondering when the venom will stop. Something within them both makes them stand and take it, not saying a word. He is an old man and maybe he has a point. It'll be over soon.

"Take your cries for charity elsewhere." He is almost out of breath. As he stands staring at the boys, his chest puffing in and out, the door opens behind him and a poodle trots to the man's feet. Scott stifles a laugh as Sid politely moves his foot away from the animal, who is beginning to lick the exposed skin between his trousers and his socks.

"Don't you dare touch her, you pathetic little weasel," the man screams at Sid.

Sid pushes past Scott onto the driveway, humiliated by the direct insult.

The man scoops up the dog with one palm and his tone of voice changes immediately. "Morons, aren't they Peggy, that's right, ab-so-lute morons," he coos.

Scott stays on the doorstep for a second longer, looking at the man, wondering how someone could be this angry so early in the morning. At this time of the day, the world is still meant to be full of hope. "I'm sorry we bothered you, Sir," he says, and walks slowly after Sid.

Sid waits around the corner for Scott. "I don't think this is a good idea," he says when he sees his friend. It was different with the guys at school, they were young and they were a gang. Safety in numbers. But there was something deeply affecting about a total stranger screaming in his face. Sid wishes he could call it a day but the thought of the Watson Brothers holds him hostage. Whose stupid idea was this anyway? Knocking on strangers' doors. As if strangers ever did him any favours. In all the years he's been taking care of his mum, all the public embarrassments and screams, no one had ever stepped in to help Sid. He crosses his arms over his chest. He knew this was how it would be. Increasingly, he is beginning to think of Scott as the devil on his shoulder, nudging him further and further along a dark path and away from everything he has taught himself to believe. Sid sighs. He needs the money. There is no alternative.

Scott bounces his rubber ball against the brick wall. "What? He was just a miserable old git. Pretty intense though."

"I know. I feel sick."

Scott stops bouncing. "Gotta confess, it's a shit tonne harder than I thought it'd be."

Sid considers their potential day ahead. It does feel good to be doing something different, just for once. Even though it goes against every sensible thought in his mind, he isn't ready to give up just yet. Besides, he really needs that money. He brushes his trousers clean. "Right. Next."

Scott smiles and follows him to the next house. This part of town seems really old. Some of the slates on the roofs are missing and there are oak trees that look like they've been here forever. Unlike his own neighbourhood, where the mark of success is a manicured lawn and a prestige saloon car, these houses show the true stamp of individuality. They look up at the eaves. In their state of mind it might as well be the peak of Everest spearing the clouds. The gate is covered in moss and it takes Sid two goes to shift it open. Branches twang back against his body as he tries to walk the path. He feels wisps against his face. "Jesus, what's that?" he says, spitting and pulling something from his mouth.

Scott is slowly making his way behind him. He has pulled the sleeves of his jumper down over his hands to protect himself. His hood is tightened around his face, and he holds it in place with his teeth. "Spider-webs," he lisps, not wanting to risk letting them enter his mouth. Much as he loves the fresh air, the solitary pleasure of walking alone, he draws the line at creepy crawlies. "Gross."

"It went in my mouth!" Sid claws at his tongue with his fingers, feeling violated. He hadn't signed up for this. Neither Scott nor Sid had been the type of boys to cremate insects through a magnifying glass; they'd both had other things to think about. Sid knocks on the door, twice.

The house looks abandoned, but they give it a minute before trudging back through the spider webs and out onto the street. Scott's sure he sees an old woman peering through the curtains at them but he hasn't the energy to tell Sid.

An old Morris Minor rattles up the road as they stand by the gate. The boys watch the driver perform a perfect three-point turn and park outside a house with a yellow door. They step aside to let her out.

She gives them a quick glance. She recognises the one with

dark hair. She worked as a doctor in a deprived part of the city for the best part of twenty years and she never forgets a face. It is something of a curse; sometimes she would rather forget the sights she saw. She remembers the boy's frown, the way he'd curled up to read his school book on the bench outside his mum's hospital room.

"Need some help?" asks Sid, wondering why the woman is staring at him like that.

She opens the boot and the boys pounce on her shopping bags before she can answer.

"Thank you," she says, genuinely grateful. It was fine living alone, perfectly fine really, but sometimes she missed the extra pair of hands. She wishes her own kids would visit more often. "Thanks," she says.

They carefully place her bags on the doorstep.

"Thank you," she says again and waits for them to leave.

"Excuse me," ventures Sid. He looks at Scott for reassurance. "We're cleaning ovens today and wondered if you would like yours cleaned for..."

She smiles. "No, love. I'm fine, thanks."

Sid's shoulders droop as he walks across the new path. He checks his watch. They've been at it for hours.

"Onwards," chirps Scott. Maybe it was the two of them together that was the problem. Separately, they might do alright: Scott with his smart talk and Sid with his honest face. No one ever trusted them when they were together. Besides, thinks Scott, it's fine having company but he could do with a minute to himself. "Wanna split up?"

By mid-afternoon, they are starving and a little regretful. They've done every house in this part of town except one.

125

Sid doesn't want to be the one to give up first. "One more then the tuck shop, yeah?"

"Sure," agrees Scott. "I'll wait here."

He is on his twentieth bounce of the ball when he hears Sid shouting his name. His friend almost falls over as he skids around the corner. "Scott! We got one!"

Scott picks up the bucket of supplies and runs towards the house. "You keep going, yeah," he shouts to Sid, grinning. "Get us some more houses. I'll come find you later. What's her name?"

"Shit, I forgot to ask."

"Get their name next time, mate, yeah?"

"Yeah," says Sid, practically running to the next house.

It was easier than Scott had imagined. Once he'd figured out how to unscrew the oven front, it was just a case of scrubbing until he could see glass or metal or whatever was meant to be under all the grime. The hard part was the small talk. Scott had imagined that they'd leave him to it, but they all lingered in the kitchen doorways, or tried to make conversation over the drone of daytime TV. He drank more cups of instant coffee than his body could take. By the fourth oven he was running on auto-pilot and he'd nailed his script. He'd realised which questions led to long answers. He would ask them how their Easter had been, he would begin to apply the finishing touches with the toothbrush and before he knew it, the job was done and he could get the hell out of there.

The rejection got easier, too. They came to realise that there were certain people who needed company and others who considered nothing worse than strangers in their home. By the time four o'clock came and Sid had to bolt home, they'd been on their feet for seven hours straight.

With a wad of money in his jacket pocket, Sid finds it difficult to say no to Scott when the phone on his pillow begins to ring at five o'clock the next morning.

Scott is on a high. "Get yourself up to Grantham Drive. I've stashed a suitcase with cleaning products for you, behind the wheelie bin in the empty house."

Sid gropes on the side table for his glasses. "You what?"

"There's a map in there, too," adds Scott. "I'm gonna do Clifton. We'll rendezvous up at the tuck shop between one and two."

Two hours later, Sid is dragging the suitcase from an overgrown garden, hoping that nobody sees him. He clicks it open. Inside is everything Scott promised, plus a small stack of papers, bound up with an elastic band. Scott is always one step ahead. Sid knows for a fact that Scott doesn't have a printer at home - the one gadget he doesn't own - but he must have begged, borrowed or stolen one, because he has printed out a hundred small slips of paper with a Clip-Art icon of an oven. He's set up an email address where clients can contact them. He's thought of everything. There is even a section to write the call-back time on, in case people are out or the decision-maker isn't home. Sid is impressed. This is the most academic thing Scott has ever done. He really means business. Sid opens the notebook and reads Scott's spider-scrawled instruction: *Use this for appointments you get. We should be keeping records.* He picks up the chewed pen from the suitcase and heads for his first house.

The sun is setting when Scott arrives at the last address on his list. Over the course of the evening he has snaked his way up to the top of a sprawling estate. He drinks the final swig from his bottle of orange juice and chucks it into a nearby hedge. He's never been up here before. It's alright, the view, a semi-reward for his hard work; orange streaks across a pink sky, the city a mass of Roman ruins, tower blocks and clustered housing jutting out of the moorland. He stretches his arms above his head and immediately regrets it. His palms are raw from scrubbing with steel wool and he is beginning to understand why his mum keeps a jar of hand cream by the kitchen sink. His whole body aches. It isn't natural to be contorted for so long. He can't wait to get home. He'll spend some of his earnings on a taxi tonight; he's had enough of the general public. Maybe tonight he'll even sleep straight through. He is exhausted. He raps three times on the door and waits. He can hear the commotion of a busy house at tea-time: children screaming that they don't want to go to bed yet, the roar of the 'Eastenders' theme tune. When the door is suddenly yanked open, Scott is completely unprepared for the person that greets him.

"Leila," he says, startled. The girl from school seems in above her depth. A chubby baby clings to her side. Leila, usually serene, is covered in baby food. She manages a smile.

"What you doing here?" she asks.

"I'm... do you need your oven cleaned?" he blurts.

"It's not my house," she says, laughing. "Jesus, do you think I'd live in a house like this? It's not my house." The baby lets out a needy cry. Leila shimmies him gently, like a pro. "I'm just babysitting," she adds.

"Cool." There is an awkward silence and they are both glad for the background noise. The baby gurgles contentedly. "You're good at that."

"Are you kidding?" Leila lowers her voice. "I bloody hate kids."

"So why are you..."

"We needed some pennies." Scott suddenly remembers Sid, the confrontation with Leila and Reashan in the stairwell, and later in the auditorium. He can't even begin to imagine what the hell it's all about.

"So I'd better..." Leila tucks her hair behind her ears and gestures towards the house.

"Of course, yep." Scott holds up his hand in a goodbye salute and immediately feels like a prat. He turns to leave and has an idea. "Hey!"

Leila is waiting to be impressed.

"Why don't you join us? Me and Sid, you know Sid, from school."

"Oh yeah, we know Sid."

"We're trying to make a bit of money too. We're going around cleaning ovens. It's pretty easy, you could come and work with us. The money's not bad and..."

Leila stops him. "I don't think that's a very good idea."

"Why not?"

Leila wonders how much Scott knows. Whether Sid has told him anything about the shop, and the trouble he's got them all in. It's not her place to say. "Just... I don't think so, Scott. And hey." She points a finger at Scott, then back to herself, one eyebrow raised. "This little meeting. Never happened. I'm meant to be at the library."

"You did what?" Sid glares at Scott. It is the first time he's been angry with his friend. The feeling takes him by surprise, a different emotion to the slowly simmering sense of inadequacy he feels most days. This is all-consuming. It makes him want to jump off the bench and grab Scott, yank him up from the grass, scream at him and find out what the hell he thinks he's playing at. Up here

129

on the hill he could get away with losing sight of himself, letting it all out for a minute.

"I don't really believe in coincidences," says Scott. "Things happen for a reason. They need money, we need helpers, so I asked her." He takes another bite of chocolate.

Sid clamps his hands onto his knees and speaks through gritted teeth. "What made you think that was a good idea? I don't want them involved in this. I've already ruined their lives."

"Calm down, she didn't even seem keen." Scott looks at his friend. "You don't want *them* involved in this or you don't want *me* involved?"

"I can't do this," Sid says, grabbing the mobile phone from his pocket and launching it at Scott.

Scott scrambles up the hill in pursuit. He blocks off the path, forcing Sid to stop. "Whatever is going on, I don't need to know."

Sid softens a little.

"Look," says Scott. He whistles a tune into the air, throws his ball up into the sky a few times. "This is me not caring. You live your life, I'll live mine. We've both got our own shit going on. What matters is this. Now."

Sid shuffles on his feet. "I'm not..." He tries again, the anger subsiding. "I'm not used to this, you know. I've had fifteen years of never talking about anything. With anyone. And now you're here and it's like my whole world's been blown open and... I can't do it. I need some distance between that..." Sid points to the town below, where his little house sits. "And this." He gestures to the space between him and Scott.

"Agreed," says Scott, tucking Sid's mobile phone carefully into his chest pocket.

Sid smiles, relieved. "Agreed." They walk towards the city together. "Shit, what if Leila says yes?"

"If she says yes, you'll have nothing to feel guilty about anymore. You won't be the one who ruined their lives. You'll be the one who helped them pick up the pieces, gave them a way to earn money again. You'll be her knight in shining armour."

CHAPTER 10

By the time Leila gets home, all she wants is silence, but she can hear them arguing from halfway up the street. That's the thing about living in a terrace. Sure, there's an endless supply of friends, and summer holidays as a kid were one long adventure, but there sure as hell is nowhere to hide. As she rummages in her bag for her house keys a neighbour passes. Leila nods politely. "Lovely evening," she says, smiling sweetly, and the neighbour returns the niceties. They both do a good job of pretending that they cannot hear the screaming match. Leila is glad to get in the door. Chaotic it may be, but there really is no place like home.

"Good study session?" her mum asks, appearing out of nowhere before Leila even has time to hang up her denim jacket.

Leila avoids eye contact. "Fine, yeah. Library was quiet."

"Did you eat?"

"I'm still hungry," says Leila, following her mum into the kitchen. She always has to keep a distance of at least a metre: her mum wears a traditional sari that trails like a viper in her wake, threatening to trip up anyone who comes too close. Leila lifts the lid on an enormous metal pot.

"Your favourite." Like the neighbour, Mrs Nanda is ignoring the fact that her son and her husband are tearing strips off each other in the sitting room next door. She dishes up an enormous bowl of daal for her daughter and watches her eat. "Good, right?"

Leila nods. She hasn't liked this dish since primary school, but she knows how much pride her mum takes in her cooking. It isn't worth the hassle. Leila cleans her bowl quickly and declines a second serving. "Hang on a second." She observes the gaping hole in the wall where the washing machine used to be. "What happened?"

Mrs Nanda tries to keep her voice calm. "Your dad took it to the pawnbroker."

Leila frowns. "It's really that bad?" She gestures to the sitting room. "Is that what they're arguing about?"

"Sort of." Mrs Nanda looks hurt on her son's behalf. Reashan had woken up this morning to find his Liverpool shirt, his pride and joy, missing from his wardrobe. Fifteen years old and Mrs Nanda had never seen her son so livid. He's been arguing with his dad non-stop since then. That's the difference with the men of this family. While the women are renowned for their steely sensibilities, calm until forced to be otherwise, the men like to get it all out. Reashan and Omar are as bad as each other, round in circles, no one willing to be the first to back down. "Will you speak to him?" Mrs Nanda asks her daughter. Not only are Leila and Reashan thick as thieves, but they are twins, and Mrs Nanda has never been able to fathom the weird and wonderful links that bind them. If anyone can talk Reashan out of a foul mood, it's Leila.

Leila braces herself and walks into the living room. Her whole family is there. Her uncle sits on an armchair in the corner of the room, looking exasperated and trying to find a break in the shouting to say his piece. He rolls his eyes at Leila as she enters. She casts her eyes around the room. Like a spot the difference picture, there are subtle changes to the room since she left this morning, which reveal the full extent of her family's financial crisis. Mrs Nanda's wedding sari hangs in its dry-cleaning bag, ready to be sold. The display cabinet, which used to house inherited gold trinkets and family heirlooms, is bare. Where the tapestry used to hang on the wall above the gas fire, now reveals a bleached outline. It's even worse than she'd thought.

"Reashan." Leila's voice is a tone louder than usual.

Her brother doesn't hear her.

"Reashan!"

He turns around, surprised to see her. For the past few days, his fists have been permanently clenched. Tonight, his eyes are red from angry tears. He's always been like that, thinks Leila, liable to explode without warning.

Reashan glares at his sister. "Nice of you to make an appearance." She's always been like that, he thinks, likely to dart out of the door the second you need help. They were meant to be a team, but, as far as he could see, he was the only one having to make any sacrifices around here. Leila has a cupboard full of rare records that she could take down the market to sell, but he doesn't see her lifting a finger. He turns to his dad. "What about her?"

Omar Nanda smiles patiently as his daughter. She has stolen a T-shirt from his wardrobe again: the black T-shirt with 'Pulp' emblazoned on the front was from the time Omar saw them play Sheffield Leadmill, only twelve people in the audience. It is impossible to be angry at his daughter. "Leave us to it, would you Leila."

"Mum said to..." she begins.

"Later, love," says her dad, beginning to calm down. He gestures to the record player. One possession that will never be sold. Some things are just too important and, for Omar Nanda, music will always be thus. "Why don't you put some music on."

Reashan scowls at his sister as she selects a record and sets it in motion.

For a few minutes all is calm. Then, out of nowhere, the argument starts up again, quietly at first and then at full throttle. Leila has had enough. She pulls on her jacket and heads for the front door. Outside, she lifts up the unused recycling box and retrieves her stash of tobacco and the plastic lighter. Her emergency supply. And this, she thinks, furrowing her brow and hugging her arms around her body as she takes a drag, is definitely an emergency.

Walking always helps. Leila heads for nowhere in particular. Out here, she can think. She can't get the wedding sari out of her mind. That dress was supposed to be hers, for her own wedding, and she is angry at her mum for conceding to sell it. It's not even about the dress, Leila thinks as she sidesteps into an alleyway and re-lights the cigarette. She can think of nothing worse than being tied down to marriage, especially the kind of wedding that would require her to wear a sari like that. A dress full stop.

Maybe it's a twin thing. She and Reashan are closer than anyone could imagine - there were days when they didn't need to talk because they knew exactly how the other was feeling. It was as though a long piece of thread had been strung between them at birth, and they had figured out how to navigate around each other without getting tangled. But Reashan pissed her off tonight. For all that Reashan talks about hating Sid Sadowskyj, Leila knows that, deep down, he feels as bad for Sid as she does.

She bumps into Scott a week later, as she's walking home from school. Something about Scott's eager hello makes her wonder if he was waiting for her. She tries not to over-analyse. "You again," she says. "Where's Sid?" It's unusual to see either of the lads alone these days.

If she's honest, she's a little jealous of their closeness and the natural camaraderie that seems to exist between them. She wishes she had a friend like that.

"I was thinking," begins Scott. He's been trying to think of a plan to get Leila on board. Already, the cleaning business is getting out of hand. He's cleaned seven ovens this morning, has nine more appointments tonight. It seemed that once word got out, people were keen to employ them. It isn't just ovens, either.Scott and Sid have been asked to clear out garages, tidy up attics and defrost freezers. They're both exhausted. Scott's out of school more often than he's in it. He's forging sick notes, feigning illness. Sid, meanwhile, is running on empty, so tired some days that he can barely string a sentence together. Scott knows that, when it comes down to it, Sid would actually love some help, even if it was from the Nandas. They'd talked about it. They have their deal. Their friendship, Scott is sure, is strong enough now to deal with anything.

Out of nowhere, Reashan appears. He puts a protective arm around his sister. "Are you coming?" he asks, ignoring Scott.

"In a minute," she answers, forcefully removing his arm from her shoulder.

He gives her a cautionary look. "In a minute?"

Leila stands her ground. "I'll catch up with you, alright?"

Reashan glares at Scott before walking away,

"Sorry, he's an idiot sometimes."

Scott is surprised. The admission seems intimate, as though Leila is somehow betraying her brother, and Scott feels bad for asking. "Listen," he begins. "I know you don't want to work with me and Sid, but... it'd be good to get *Reashan* on board. He looks like he could use something to focus on." Scott lightens the tone. "Plus... it's actually pretty fun. Good work experience."

Leila doesn't look convinced.

"You know." He tries to scope her out. "For uni or work or whatever you wanna do." Scott reaches into his pocket.

Leila's eyes widen at the sight of a wad of twenty pound notes.

"It's pretty easy money," admits Scott. It's true. Sure, he is knackered by the end of the day but people do much worse things for cash. "Reashan could come and clean with us, and you could do the admin stuff. If you wanted." He studies Leila's expression. If he was right, her love for her brother and her desire to be independent would outweigh her sense of pride or fear of Scott or whatever it was that was holding her back. "Will you speak to him?" He counts to ten and waits for her to say yes.

Reashan, it turned out, was not just up for the idea; he grabbed the opportunity with both fists and quickly established himself as a jack of all trades. When he wasn't in a mood, Reashan was up for almost anything. Between the three of them, Reashan, Scott and Sid divvied up tasks and responsibilities with military precision. Once the money began to roll in they put Reashan in charge of operations. Leila watched with pride as her brother made notes in his Moleskin diary and took calls on his new mobile. Eventually, even she had to concede that it was a better idea than babysitting and, as the team grew to include most of their classmates, Leila took on the task of completing everyone's coursework in return for cash by the hour. It worked out well for everyone involved.

They are nervous about telling their parents. For the first week, they make do with covert trips to the pawn shop, buying back their parents' possessions one item at a time so as not to arouse suspicion. They begin to invent increasingly ridiculous ways to give their parents money: someone had dropped fifty quid outside the bank; they'd overpaid on the last school trip and were due a refund - school was giving out money to high achievers as an incentive to keep studying. It is Leila who eventually has enough of lying.

Sitting at the kitchen table facing their parents, they are both terrified.

Omar Nanda is shell-shocked. He stares at the pile of money on the table. It's enough to get them out of trouble, to get the shop up and running again. It changes everything. And his kids are sitting here telling them that the money will keep on coming. He looks at his wife. Her face is composed, but there is a slight twinge in the corner of her mouth. Mrs Nanda will take a bit of convincing, he can tell. Omar looks across the table at the pair of them. Leila with her rebellious streak, Reashan more focused than he's been in years. It's impossible to be cross with them for going behind their backs when he feels so much damn pride.

CHAPTER 11

Karen remembers the first time she realised that her life was over. It was in the hazy first weeks after her baby came, when the days blurred into night so seamlessly that she suspected foul play. Lucasz was sitting on the sofa in their rented flat, watching her as she struggled to remember the correct position for feeding: all the while, this boy, Sidney they'd called him, looked up at her with placid eyes as if to say, "I'm not going anywhere." Lucasz had just sat there, flicking through the TV channels while she tried to pretend that none of this was happening, and Karen realised, then, that it was only a matter of time before he left. She'd seen the warning signs for the past nine months, while her belly swelled and she lost her figure and her friends stopped calling and Lucasz went out dancing with other girls instead of her. But she'd thought it would change. That the baby would mend everything.

She'd called her mum that night, begged to be allowed to come back home to live, to the too-small terraced house she'd grown up in. She'd packed her bags and left that night while her husband was sleeping.

Over the years, Karen had convinced herself that it was Lucasz who left. His dramatic exit had become woven into the tapestry of fact and fiction that was Karen's past. Sid had grown up believing that he had been abandoned. It was a necessary secret, a self-preservation device. Karen had a lot of those.

Over the months that followed, Lucasz tried everything to see his son. He politely knocked on the front door. He returned with flowers for Karen, gifts for the baby, mix-tapes of songs he thought they both should hear. Then he started turning up at night, throwing stones up at the window where Karen and the boy were trying to sleep. Karen lay awake listening to him swearing in Ukrainian and wishing she was back in their bed, Lucasz whispering to her in that alien language, words that always swept her away from herself. Then he turned up angry, smashed a brick through the living room window at four in the morning. Then he stopped coming round at all. The last Karen had heard, Lucasz had skipped town. On a shopping trip with her mum, Karen had spotted his beloved guitar in the window of a pawn shop. That was fifteen years ago, and now all that was left of him was this teenage boy who had inherited Lucasz's intelligent frown and the empty guitar case under the bed.

Of course he left. He was the leaving type.

She just had to keep telling herself that.

Sid clears the coffee table, making a mental note of the position of his mum's stuff so that he can place it all back once he's finished. He arranges his money in neat piles. He thinks back to two weeks ago, his reluctance to believe they could make it happen and the despondency he had felt after that first door. The old man, screaming at him as though Sid embodied everything that was wrong with the world.

With the Watson Brothers appeased by the steady delivery of forty pounds in cash under the crate every day without fail, Sid manages to convince himself that the situation is under control. As far as his home life is concerned, nothing has changed. Sid approaches his new commitments with the same tenacity and regimented order that he applies to every other aspect of his life. He has a carefully-planned timetable of those lessons he can skip to avoid getting into trouble. Lucky for Sid, his presence over the past few years has been so low-profile that teachers rarely even notice his absence. He skips lunch and works straight through instead. At four, he returns home, selects a bottle of vodka from the growing supply and tends to his mum. She remains none the wiser. With the extra money in his pocket, Sid begins to leave his mum treats around the house: the shower gel is scented; the jam has real fruit in it. He buys her a pair of fluffy bed socks and a bright pink bath towel. He bins the receipts, cuts off the labels and tells her that they're charity shop finds. In the early evening, once Karen has crashed out, Sid pulls on his jacket and heads out again. It's a simple routine, but Sid feels more alive than he ever has and he is fully aware that he has Scott to thank for that. If Sid and Scott had been inseparable before, the past weeks have made them siamese, fused them together for good, for better or worse.

He feels the weight of the notes in his hand. Crisp banknotes, as though they've been ironed flat. He's been stockpiling his earnings. The first week of cleaning, he couldn't shake the suspicion that he and Scott had been tricked, that it had all been an elaborate con to teach him a lesson, that a trip to the bank would reveal their earnings to be Monopoly money, unspendable. He peels the top note from the first pile and holds it up to the window. For the first time in his life he notices the details, the elaborate coils on the man's hair, the way the turquoise bleeds into blue. His mobile phone rings.

"You busy?" chirps Scott.

Sid can tell that he's walking. Scott is in business mode.

"What do you reckon it takes to get your face on a fifty-pound note?" he asks Scott, placing the note back onto the pile and securing it with an elastic band.

Scott's not listening. "Job's come up. I need you. Like, now."

They have an agreement. Sid is off-duty after midnight. "Can't Leila and Reashan do it?"

"Can't. Family thing. Phones are off."

"Scott, I'm. I'm kinda busy here." It's one in the morning. Leaving now would be an unknown entity. Karen sleeps straight for the first few hours but after that it's anyone's guess. She's woken up Sid dozens of times in the early morning before school, because she's scared, because she's worried, because she's crying. She needs him.

"It's five hundred quid. Straight up."

"In the middle of the night?"

"Hey, I didn't ask too many questions. I don't really wanna know. It's easy money, we've just gotta shift a few boxes. You coming or what?"

Sid does the sums. That money would certainly let him off the Watson Brothers' hook for a while and give him some breathing space. He can't keep going at the rate he is. He's falling behind with his studies. "One second," he says. Sid races quietly up the stairs, peeks in on his mum. He watches the bedsheets rising and falling to check that she's still breathing. "I love you, mum," he whispers.

Back downstairs, he returns to the phone. "Where and when?" he asks Scott.

The house is silent when Karen wakes up. Without opening her eyes she reaches for the bottle on the table beside her bed. Christ, her head hurts. She squints open her eyelids just wide enough to locate her glass, and edges herself slowly onto her elbow. She pours until the bottle is empty. Enough to see her through til morning. She rolls onto her side, buries herself beneath the blankets and closes her eyes again.

The next time she awakes, she is less calm. The dreams are becoming increasingly more vivid these days, so that she struggles to separate the real from the imagined. Instinctively, her hand reaches for the bottle, and she is distressed to find it empty. Karen has a hazy recollection of earlier that evening. How long ago had that been? The days bleed into each other. It could have been five hours or five weeks ago. Karen squints at the curtains for a clue. The light outside is weak and pale, the room heady with the sweat of a too-hot summer's night. The back of her neck is damp. She needs some help.

"Sidney," she croaks.

No answer.

Karen heaves herself up in her bed. "Sidney, son. Come here and help your mum."

She waits. Her son is a light sleeper. It only ever takes him a few minutes. He'll trot through in his boxer shorts, his eyes still sleepy like when he was a little lad, and he'll ask her what she needs and go get it for her. That's how it works. She listens out for the creak of his bed. Nothing.

Now Karen is scared. To her surprise, something makes her stand up and walk to his room. She isn't sure if it's selfishness or maternal instinct, but she wants to see what's holding him up. She stands over his neatly-made bed and shakes at the duvet, already knowing that he is not in there but wanting to be certain. She wanders into the hallway, splays her toes against the carpet at the top of the stairs and shouts his name again. Pitch black down there. Now she is worried. She stands still in his room and listens. She can hear the clock ticking and she checks it, just to be sure it isn't daytime and that she hasn't completely lost her mind. 2:47am. Sid should be in his bed.

For the first time in years, Karen needs fresh air. It'll help her think. Back in her past life, the sea air was the only thing that cleared her mind. It had always been something she sought out. She'd go for long walks around the city after school, drive out to the coast at weekends and just stand there, a tune in her head and the sea salt stinging her tongue. She and Lucasz had got married in a registry office further up the coast, the wind belting her dress against her bare legs. She couldn't remember the last time she'd seen the sea. There'd been a trip with Sidney, fish and chips at the harbour in Whitby, but that was a while ago now.

Karen reaches for the window. She halts. There is someone in the garden, she's sure of it this time. She can hear voices out there. She keeps herself hidden and peeks, terrified, out of the window. The curtain exhales with her shallow breathing, fluttering against the windowpane. Karen holds her breath.

There are two men out in the yard and they are arguing about something. The stocky man is placing what looks like a crate inside their shed, and the smaller man is picking something light and flimsy from the floor. And now they are closing the broken latch on the shed and placing a brick against it to keep it closed.

Karen is mesmerised. It seems so real, like dreaming in Technicolour. She closes her eyes and takes a few deep breaths. When she looks out again, the yard is empty. She blinks, unsure what to make of it. She can't handle this right now.

CHAPTER 12

Scott is both exhausted and elated when he arrives home. It doesn't matter that it's half one in the morning and that he hasn't slept properly in weeks. Easy money. He picks an apple from the fruit bowl and tosses it playfully in the air. His mind is spinning with ideas. He's getting through a sketchbook a day, each page crammed beyond the margins with film plots, drawings and lists. With his days full of appointments, Scott sees himself as a scavenger, picking the bones out of each interaction and finding inspiration in every second. Even the crap days teach him important stuff, like patience, and the fact that you can't carry a grand piano up three flights of stairs. It is no longer about the money. The new pile of books on his bedroom floor has titles like, 'Speaking for Success' and 'The Powerful Manager'. He isn't ashamed. His investigation extends outward, too. Scott has used the long June evenings to decipher the universal code of body language, studying the movements of people out in The Shambles, assessing the dynamics of groups. It is all part of the plan. He is arming himself. He takes a bite of the apple.

"Scott."

Scott turns round at the sound of his dad's voice. He'd thought he was still away. But no. Malcolm sits at the head of the unset dinner table, his arms spread over the chair as though it is a throne.

Elaine is sitting in the chair next to him. It's too early for this. Scott's usually the only one up at this time, either sneaking in after a late-night job or up at the kitchen table formulating the day's schedule. Something's not right.

"Sit down, Scott," instructs Elaine.

Scott protests. "I was just about to…"

His father's voice is firm. "Sit down."

Scott pulls out the chair opposite his dad and sits down, annoyed at the interruption to his thoughts. The whole walk home, Scott had been mapping out a new idea in his mind, ironing out the creases. He needs to get it down on paper before he forgets it forever. That's the thing about Scott's ideas. They're like dynamite: they may have a long fuse, but once they take light they disappear irretrievably. He wonders what could be so important. "What is it?" he huffs.

"Your mother and I are separating."

Scott keeps his cool and says nothing. Out of the corner of his eye, he can see his mum's hand trembling at her face as she begins to cry and tries to cover it.

Malcolm continues, his voice flat and dispassionate, as though he's reading out the terms and conditions on a new business deal. Scott hates him more than ever. The haggard lines on his face. The piercing blue eyes that make women trust him more than they should. The pathetic receding hairline that he tries to hide. He's like a walking, talking mid-life crisis. "I've already moved out my things and will be away on business tomorrow."

Scott absorbs this information. Elaine holds her hand out to her son, more for her comfort than his. He takes it.

"Sorry, Scott." She rummages up her sleeve for a tissue. "I'm really, really sorry." She lets out a loud sob. Scott strokes the top of her hand with his thumb, noticing for the first time in his life how small his mum's hands are. Her usually-perfect crescent fingernails are bitten at the ends.

Malcolm stares coldly across the room, wanting to be anywhere but here. The fostering thing had always been her idea. Malcolm had just gone along with it. She'd wanted to adopt, but that would have meant years of probing into his personal life. No way was he going to let that happen. Agreeing to look after Scott was the least he could do. It was Malcolm who couldn't have children.

Scott breaks the silence. "Do we have champagne?"

His mum and dad both turn to look at him. "We stayed together for you," says Elaine.

"I've waited years for this," Scott continues. He can't remember a time when his parents were happy together. It seemed to him that their marriage was a joke from the start. Scott had almost given up on them admitting it to themselves. Forget all the moping, this is news to *celebrate*.

"Son," says Elaine, pulling her hand away. "You're upset, don't say anything..."

Malcolm stares him down. "Go on," he challenges. "Let him speak."

Scott takes a deep breath. "You're a prick, dad. A total prick. Always have been. Just because you did this one good thing, you took me in when no one else would, you think that redeems you."

Malcolm's eyes narrow. His jaw clenches.

Scott is unfazed. It's been years since his dad has had time to listen to anything he's had to say. He takes his chance. "Mum tiptoes around you with your black cloud and treats you like a god. Whenever you're here you can't wait to be away again. You can't stand being anywhere near me. You've never even tried with me. So frankly I'm relieved that I don't have to deal with you and the misery you spread."

A cold silence pervades the room.

Elaine shuffles in her chair. "Maybe we should all just…"

Malcolm's voice is coated in venom. "When we took you in, I had hoped for a son. Someone I could be proud of. Proud enough to call my own. You know what? The people at work, they don't even know you exist. I never talk about you. You're a crushing disappointment to me." He stares at his son.

Elaine jumps to Scott's defence. "Malcolm! How dare you…"

"No." Malcolm's hand slams on the table. "If we're outing truths, it's time I said my piece. I am sick of watching you with your outlandish thoughts, your stupid ideas and your irresponsibility. You bounce through life without a thought for anyone else and without a care." Malcolm's anger reaches new heights. He is seething. "You live in a dream world. You do nothing but chase stupid bloody dreams!"

Scott stares straight ahead, not knowing how to feel, let alone how to react.

The tirade continues. "You don't try at school, you are spoilt, you have no talent and you're so bloody irritating." Malcolm knows he should stop, but that's the problem isn't it, that his son's so goddamn hypersensitive. It'll do him good to know what people really think of him. Toughen him up a bit. Malcolm gives his best shot. "I look at your mother and I see you. That's why we're separating." He enjoys watching the colour drain from his son's face as he delivers his knockout blow. "You should have been a fucking *abortion*," he screams, kicking Scott's chair as he heads for the front door, glad that it's finally all over, that he doesn't have to pretend any more.

Upstairs in his room, Scott's is a rage that coils around his insides and leaves him gasping for air. He pulls at his hair, tugging at the roots, harder than they should be able to withstand. There is the taste of metal in his mouth. Scott stifles his screams with a pillow, hating himself for not being able to protect his mum, for allowing history to repeat itself, for letting it all affect him despite his best efforts. Weak. He yanks his head back.

The Shakespeare quote on his ceiling stops him for a second. Greatness. He scoffs. Scott wonders if maybe he should just call it quits. Fifteen years of fucking it up for everyone, and he's not sure how much more he can take. He thinks about his best friend, Sid silently seething that he'd been called out so late, completely distracted the entire evening, hardly a dozen words spoken between them the whole night. Worries that he might have fucked that up too. He wants to get out of the house, to be anywhere else. On the TV, Morpheus is asking Neo to choose between a red pill and a blue pill.

He waits for his mum to knock on his door, to act like a parent and take his side, but it is Sid who interrupts. Scott's phone is on the loudest setting on the pillow, but he doesn't hear it ring. His head is too cacophonous for that. He sees the blue square flashing in the pitch blackness, his friend's name on the screen.

Sid's voice is frantic.

"Slow down, mate," Scott tells him. "Catch your breath. Breathe. C'mon, Sid, breathe." The noise in Scott's head disappears as soon as he hears Sid's next words. Scott gasps, everything else that has happened tonight suddenly becoming completely irrelevant. Greatness, Scott thinks, is knowing when something is bigger than yourself. He can hear the terror in his friend's voice, and Scott is out of his bed, pulling on the first clothes he finds and running out of the door and into the street before Sid even has to ask. He makes his voice as calm as possible, though in truth he is scared too. "I'll be there in ten," he says, running towards the hospital as fast as he can.

"You're right," says Sid, out of nowhere.

Scott glances at his friend. Sid is paler than ever, as though he's sitting in a different room to everyone else, under a different sun. The hospital lights don't help. "What's that, buddy?"

"The seats," says Sid. "They're always blue." He drums his fingers against the pale blue fabric and glances around the room. Friday night in Accident & Emergency and Sid had forgotten that people like this existed. The whole spectrum of human casualty. It had been years since her last binge. Sid had made it an impossibility, carefully controlling Karen's access to the stuff. He makes eye contact with a man in his thirties, his face covered in scars, who clutches a dirty bandage on his wrist. Sid looks away. "How much longer are they gonna make us wait?" he asks Scott, angrily. They'd told him to stay put, that they would tell him as soon as they had any news, but it has been forty minutes and twenty-one seconds now and Sid is beginning to think that they're hiding something from him.

Scott still isn't sure how bad it is. It had happened so quickly. The phone call, Sid changing his story every two minutes: his mum was ill, his mum was dying, his mum had had an accident. Scott had arrived in time to catch a glimpse of Mrs Sadowskyj as she was carried from the ambulance on a stretcher. He couldn't see much, with all the theatre staff rushing out the second they saw her, but Scott could guess from the gauntness of her face that Mrs Sadowskyj had been ill for a while. The way Sid was acting, it was as though it was his fault. Scott is glad that he can be here, happier still that Sid had the guts to call him. Sid's dad is nowhere to be seen. Sid hasn't even mentioned him.

"She's in good hands," Scott says, thinking as soon as he says it that the words don't mean enough. Mrs Sadowskyj is behind closed doors, possibly on an operating theatre, probably being prodded and tested and Scott has no idea really, he's just saying what they say on hospital dramas, hoping to hell that it's true. "No news is good news?" he offers. He grabs a ripped magazine from the stack in front of him. The games show host is flanked by male models. They are all grinning like morons. He throws the magazine back onto the pile. God, he hates hospitals.

"Sadu... Saydo... Sadovusuj?" The doctor stands in the centre of the waiting room.

Sid is relieved. He'd worried that they'd be sent some junior doctor, fresh out of med school. The man attempting to pronounce his name must be in his forties, with the eye bags to prove it. Sid jumps up.

Scott puts the doctor out of his misery. "It's Sadowskyj," he says quietly, as they follow him along a maze of corridors.

Sid looks down at the series of coloured lines taped to the hospital floor. Red. Yellow. Blue. Green. Black. He wonders which destination is worse. Red for blood. Black for when the lights go out. The doctor appears to be walking as though in slow motion, as though he's seen worse cases, or is it because there's no rush, not if she's dead. Sid is glad for the reassuring sound of Scott behind him, his boots squeaking predictably with every step into the unknown. He breathes a little easier. He turns to Scott. "You know that agreement we had?"

"Time to scrap it?"

"Think so."

"You know." Scott puts an arm around Sid for a second, squeezes the bones of his friend's shoulder. "There's this saying. *Burn the boats.* I never really got it before now. It's about the point of no return.

151

There's no going back so let's throw ourselves into it. Do or die."

"Burn the boats," Sid repeats, as they approach the Intensive Care ward and a nurse holds open the door for them.

CHAPTER 13

Scott insists on walking him home. When Sid takes out his keys from his pocket, Scott makes a mental note of the street name, in case he has to find it again in a hurry. The terraces all look the same around here. Scott wants to be sure he secures it to memory. He follows his friend down a grotty back street. "You know, we've never done this."

"What?" asks Sid.

"Gone to your house."

Sid is embarrassed. "What? Course we have."

"Nope, never."

Sid hovers outside his back gate. "You don't have to come in," he tells Scott, pleading with his eyes.

Scott looks directly at him. They've come too far together to turn back now. Doesn't Sid realise that? He makes his position crystal clear. "Yes. I do, mate."

Before he allows Scott in the house, Sid runs around frantically trying to tidy up. He'd found his mum and dialled the ambulance. Gone straight to the hospital with her. Left everything, hadn't even thought about it. It was just her on the living room floor, lying there like that. He'd thought she was dead. The house still bears the evidence of Karen's binge. Empty vodka bottles cover the kitchen counter, and the radio is still blaring. Sid piles all the evidence into a black bin bag, walks silently back out of the house and past Scott. He dumps the rubbish in the back street. "OK, you can come in now," he mutters, not knowing where to look.

Scott pretends not to notice the stain on the floor from where someone has recently been sick. While Sid fusses in the kitchen making tea, Scott drags the armchair forward a foot, to cover it up. He'd been prepared for the worst, but the interior of Sid's house is surprisingly clean. It stinks of cigarettes, but there is nothing to suggest that it isn't a happy home.

Scott makes himself comfortable, prepared to stay for as long as it takes. The world might as well be these four walls as far as he's concerned. Sid's just had the worst night of his life. Nothing else matters. Testing out the cushions he notices a packet of photographs, shoved almost out of sight, down the side of the sofa. It's been ripped open hastily, with little care taken, the photographs shoved back into the sleeve leaving creased edges. Scott is surprised. He knows how much pride Sid takes in his photographs: he approaches his hobby with an archivist's precision, indexing his images into unfathomable categories of colour and light. Scott intends to just tidy up the packet, straighten them out and put them back, but something catches his eye. He looks at the top image. It shows the mismatched patterns of an old person's bed, the muted colours of forgotten treasures. The photo seems to show someone buried alive. A single strand of long hair is in focus at the edge of the print. Sid has a real eye for composition.

"Here you are..." Sid is carrying a tea tray.

Scott shoves the photographs back to their hiding place, just in time. "Thanks, mate," he says, taking a cup from the tray. Sid has even gone to the length of making a couple of slices of toast. Scott wonders if he's alright. He's seems to be taking all this remarkably well.

The second Sid stops playing host and sits down, it hits him. It's the look of concern on Scott's face. Long as there was distance between his house and everything else, Sid could just about hack it. It was simple. Like parallel universes, an Escher-style globe flipping north to south with the turn of his house key. Now Scott's here, waiting for an explanation, and Sid feels like none of it was real, like he was living in a snow globe the whole time, in a state of suspended animation. Now someone's shaken it all up and he's lost his bearings, can't figure out if he's meant to be turning the key to north or south, like he's walking upside down on stairs that lead to nowhere. It's now or never. Nothing left to lose. "I hate it," he begins.

Sid doesn't know where to start. It feels so wrong, someone other than his mum in the house, and he feels self-conscious at the shabbiness of the furniture. "I hate being here," he confesses quietly. "I hate her mood swings, the lies, the secrets. The mess." His hands clench into fists at his sides. He is getting angry now. "The cleaning up when she's puked, the looks from the neighbours, the hiding, the poverty."

Scott sits still on the sofa beside him. Fifteen years of holding it all in and he can tell Sid needs this, this release. It hurts Scott to see him like this. All the pain rising to the surface.

Sid's voice is seething. "The tiptoeing around! The loneliness. The dysfunctional... shit storm!" He kicks at the coffee table.

Scott tries to calm him. "I know."

"No, you don't know." Sid shakes his head. What's the fucking

155

point, he thinks. This is his life. Nothing will ever change. His mum will return home and it'll begin all over again. It always does. "You don't know. It's horrible! The whole thing is horrible, it's always been horrible as long as I can remember!"

Scott does his best to comfort him.

"I wish I could be like you," Sid says. He is out of breath, looking around the room, imagining it all through objective eyes, the way it must look, the way they live. "But look at what she's done to me. She's ruined me. I'm fucking useless. I've no confidence, no dad! I'm useless."

"Hold on buddy, I've got to stop you there."

"It's true," spits Sid. "I'm nothing. *I'm nothing.*"

Scott searches for the words. A lifetime of trying to think positively, and you'd think he'd know exactly what to say. But it's hard. Sid's in a right state. Scott doesn't want to make him worse. He grabs him before Sid has any chance to object, holds his head against his chest. "You ain't nothing," he whispers, stroking his hair.

"I am. I'm nothing."

"Sid, you're not useless, you ain't nothing. Just… have a look at what we've created."

Sid shoots him down. "*You* created. I'm just your mate." Sid is impatient now. Maybe it wasn't such a good idea to let Scott come round. He could cry just fine all by himself. He doesn't need anyone to hold his hand. Maybe when he was eight, yeah, when she came home from the hospital with a fucking oxygen tank and he was supposed to navigate his way around the tubes. Not anymore.

"Do you think I would've done any of this if it wasn't for you?" Scott tells him.

"You were already doing it, Scott."

"They're already building cars, Sid," scoffs Scott. "Don't mean they can't get any better."

"What? What does that mean?"

Scott speaks slowly. "My foster parents split up."

Sid's mood changes instantly. He looks up. "What? You serious?"

"Yep. They told me tonight."

"Christ, I'm sorry." Sid feels awful for burdening his friend. "Then all this with my mum. Why didn't you say?"

Scott shrugs. "Cos you're my best mate in the whole world. And as far as I'm concerned that's just more important."

Sid blushes.

"And I've been thinking about it a lot anyway. And for some reason it feels good." Scott laughs despite himself, feeling a sense of freedom now that it's all out in the open. "It feels amazing."

Sid laughs along nervously, wiping his eyes on his sleeves. "How can it feel good?"

"Because we're products of our environment."

"You've said that before."

"And my dad said I was a dreamer. Or words to that effect anyway."

"And?"

"And I am."

"No…"

"I am and so are you."

Sid's mind is clear for the first time in years, like it's been encased in a helium balloon and the walls have finally popped. He's no idea how to claw his way out of the mess he's in, how to help his mum, how he's meant to face the world in a few hours like nothing has happened. All he knows is that he doesn't want to go back to the way things used to be. "We're Dreamchasers."

Scott grins. Dreamchasers. Yes! "Let's make a list."

"What?"

"A list." Scott is on his feet, holding out his hand to Sid.

"A list of what?" asks Sid as he stands.

"A list of everything we wanna do. Yeah?"

"OK."

"A list of everything we wanna do and see and let's just go for it, yeah?"

"What am I writing?" asks Sid. Now they're here, Scott leaning over his shoulder at the tiny kitchen table, the pair of them looking at a blank piece of paper, the task seems monumental.

"Things we wanna see and things we wanna do." First one is easy, thinks Scott, grinning widely. He's been composing the list in his head since he could learn to speak. He just didn't have a name for it. *Dreamchasers*. It's sublime. "Ultimate aim. Make our own movie before we're thirty."

"Everything else leads up to that?"

"Exactly. What else?"

"Why thirty?" asks Sid.

"Just puts a time frame on it." Scott finds a packet of ginger-nut biscuits in a cupboard, rips it open, hands one to Sid. "We should stay in Buckingham Palace."

"Don't think you can actually stay there," chuckles Sid.

"Well no. But just... seeing it would be cool, yeah?"

"Well I'll write 'London'."

"Why London?"

"Well, we might as well see the whole place if we're there."

"Yeah. Right," says Scott. The biscuits are stale. Doesn't even matter. "I want a good suit as well. Put a suit down. I want a suit." He'd watched 'Alfie' last week. Michael Caine, the suit, the whole lot, breaking the fourth wall, breaking every rule in the book.

Sid beams. "I wanna see a girl." He hesitates. It feels weird saying it out loud. "I want to see a girl... naked."

"What, that's it? Just naked?"

"I wanna..." Sid shifts in his chair. "I wanna... have sex with a girl."

"Get it down," says Scott, matter-of-factly. "Have some sex with girl."

"Sex with girl," Sid reads out loud.

"Sex with girl."

"How about we go to... a pub?" suggests Sid.

"Vodka martini!"

"Shaken not stirred," adds Sid quickly, eager to show Scott that he has watched *some* films in his life. He's not sure about the vodka martini. He'll see how he feels on the day. James Bond, though. The volcano cracking open to reveal a secret lair. That'd been one of the good days, Sid and his mum on the edge of the sofa, stuffing their bellies with popcorn instead of turkey one Christmas Day.

Scott slaps him on the back. "Bada boom shaken not stirred!"

They are on a roll now, the paper quickly filling with neat blocks of writing, piecing together like a game of Tetris. A list of adventures, experiences and escapades that Scott and Sid promise to embark on.

"It's a work in progress," explains Scott. "We cross them off as we go along, add to it whenever we want."

"Within reason," cautions Sid.

Scott looks at Sid, serious for a second. He rests his hands on the table. For once they're not twitching, not beyond his control. Fuck knows where his bouncy ball is. "Look Sid, I know you've not had the best of weeks." Scott scratches at his stubble. He doesn't know how to say this. He'd never even come close to saying anything like this before. Never thought he would. "Like, I just wanted to say, er. Seriously. You're my best mate. I just think you're amazing. And..."

Sid stops him. "Scott... you know I'm not gay?"

"It's not a gay thing."

"OK."

Scott smiles at his friend, takes his hands off the table. "Just kinda, take it as a compliment."

"OK." Sid smiles back. "Yeah."

The room is still, with the weight of anticipation. It feels as though they've crossed a border, stuck their heads over the parapet to discover that they are no longer under siege, that the enemy has fled.

A noise from outside, smashed glass on concrete, breaks the silence.

"What the hell is that?" asks Scott, turning in the direction of the commotion. It seems to be coming from right outside. Now he can hear voices.

"Postman," says Sid quickly. "Must be a parcel?"

Scott looks at Sid quizzically. If Scott didn't know him better, he'd think Sid was hiding something. "I'm going out to investigate. Stay here if you want."

Nicky Watson whistles a warning to his brother at the sight of the stocky blonde lad marching across the yard towards them. He knew they should've been quieter. His brother's clumsiness always gets them in trouble. He's had the feeling someone's been watching them for days. The curtain in the upstairs bedroom is always twitching.

Scott is fearless. "Who's the gorilla?" he jokes to Sid with a nod to Gavin Watson, his boots crunching over broken glass as he approaches the strangers. The things that should terrify Scott have always bounced right off him. It's as though his forcefield was wrongly calibrated at birth. The nerve of him, it's a miracle he hasn't got into more fights. Seven to date and he'd walked away unscathed every time. Mentally, at least. "Hey!" he shouts.

"Piss off," warns Nicky, pocketing the money from the floor of the shed. He gestures to his brother, jerks his head to say let's go.

There's no time for trouble. Collateral damage before sunrise? He'd rather not. Gavin lowers the crate he is carrying onto the concrete. "Sidney!" Nicky shouts over Scott's head.

Sid nods in submission.

"Tell your boyfriend here to mind his own business."

"Come inside," pleads Sid to Scott, pulling his jumper sleeves over his hands. He isn't afraid to admit that the Watson Brothers have got under his skin in a way that makes Nigel Ball pale into insignificance. He'd rather stay out of their way, just in case. It's their unpredictability that scares him most. He'd always felt kind of safe with his mum in the house. Like, nobody would hurt someone who was so defenceless. They'd take one look at her and hold their hands up in apology. Wrong house lads, move along. With Karen in the hospital, Sid feels vulnerable, his guard torn down, his bodyguard gone AWOL. "It's nothing Scott."

Scott senses the fear in his friend's voice, takes a step back.

Gavin sees his chance, shoving the boy to the ground with one swipe. It's too easy. He lands on the broken bottle, flat on his arse, and Gavin can't help but laugh. He slams the gate behind him.

Scott watches as they depart, stunned. His palm hurts. He holds it up to the dawn light, winces as he scrapes his nail under the skin, picks a sliver of glass out from the line that's meant to tell him how long he will live, how many kids he will have, some psychic crap like that.

Sid is helping him up, scraping at the yard with a dustpan and brush.

"Just stop, Sid."

"I've gotta get it cleared up, it can't stay here." Sid is picking at the tiny pieces of broken glass with his hands, struggling to see in the weak light.

"Stop!" Scott snatches at the dustpan, so that Sid has to stop.

Sid looks at him with exhausted eyes. "Just leave if you want to."

"I'm not going anywhere. What the hell was that all about?"

CHAPTER 14

Once he had told Scott about his dilemma with the Watson Brothers, Sid had no choice but to rewind to the beginning.

Scott listens intently, resisting the urge to shake his friend, to interrupt at every twist and turn in the narrative, to ask why the hell he didn't ask for help. No wonder Sid's been so distant. Most people would have crumbled under the weight of an alcoholic mum, let alone all the other insanity Sid's had to carry. It's gonna be alright, he wants to tell him. I'm gonna make it alright for you.

The metal outbuildings sit at the far end of the backstreet, overgrown with nettles. Sid picks his way carefully to his garage, bows his head as the door swings open. He's been transporting the crates from the shed first thing every morning, under the cover of darkness. He pulls on the light so that Scott can see. The garage is heaving with the stuff now. There's enough vodka in there to see Moscow through winter.

Scott begins to piece it all together, still trying to reconcile the Sidney he knows with this tangled knot of violence that seems to weave him into a criminal underworld. "So, this is what your mum got into?"

Sid nods. "She must have heard them that night." He looks

ashamed. He should never have left her. "They wanted me to sell it for them."

Scott scrunches up his eyes, trying to understand. He taps his finger against his temple. "So, what you're telling me is that you have a massive stash of illegal vodka and no idea what to do with it?"

"I know." Sid shuffles on his feet, feels his fists clench again. He feels bad for dragging Scott into this mess, wishes he could undo everything. "I'm an idiot. What the hell am I gonna do?"

Scott smiles as the idea comes to him, a little embarrassed on Sid's behalf that he even has to explain it. "You know when you go to an art gallery, and you're looking so close at the painting that all you can see are brush strokes, you aren't even really sure what you're looking at?"

"What's that got to do with anything?" Sid doesn't admit that he has never even been to an art gallery. Everything he knows about art and photography, he's learnt through books.

Scott spells it out. "We just need to find a way to turn your problem into the Watson Brothers' problem. It's simple economics. Supply and demand. We cut off the gorillas' means of supply, and we create a monopoly on our product, sell it back to them at an inflated price. Everyone wins. Well, we win. Watson Brothers, not so much. You get rid of the vodka and you get them off your back for good." He grins. "We're talking big. Sistine Chapel big. This is a job for Nigel Ball."

"We?" asks Sid, wondering what he's done to deserve a friend like Scott. "What's Nigel got to do with it?"

The call to action takes Nigel by surprise. He's been silently fuming over the rising popularity of the new boy. Scott Elliott has been flashing his cash around school. He's got himself a proper little posse working for him; some cleaning business or something. Worse still, Scott seems to be building a protective bubble around Nigel's favourite piece of shit, little skanky Sadow.

He'd thought they were joking at first. Scott had approached him in the canteen. Alone, undaunted by Nigel's reputation, he'd explained that they had a "proposition" for him. It was only when Scott brandished a wad of cash on the table that Nigel stopped daydreaming about ways to inflict pain on the new boy and began to take them seriously.

Men like him aren't meant to get scared. He's been six foot two since he was eleven. Nigel swears with every step he takes, wishing it wasn't so dark. He can hardly see the trees in front of him, but he can sense the bats hanging up there in the branches, waiting for him to make a false move. The woods are the kind of place you would dump a body. Thick enough to get lost in and close enough to the main road to park a van for an easy getaway.

Crowbar. Hammer. Balaclava. Gloves. Nigel can feel the weight of them in the rucksack on his shoulders. There'd been something else too. A CD player. Strict instructions to put on the headphones and press Play when the time comes.

He tries the torch again. The batteries had lasted for all of two minutes. With no sign of the distillery, Nigel is beginning to wonder if it's all a prank. He squints his eyes against the darkness, wishing he'd taken Scott's advice and done a reconnaissance mission in daylight. He suddenly remembers the light on the mobile phone. They'd given him the phone, just in case, with Scott's number pre-saved on speed dial. You could never be too careful, he'd said. Sid had reassured him that the Watson Brothers were out of town, but there was always the risk that they'd change their mind. Men like them are erratic, Scott had said. It's part of their intimidation, the reason for their success. Nigel's not scared. His dad could have half of York on speed dial, if it came to that. Nothing to fear. Except for the bats. He can't fucking stand bats.

The feeble beam of light from the phone lands on the dirty red bricks of a building up ahead. You've got to be kidding me, he thinks, realising with a shiver exactly where he is. His whole childhood, he'd heard friends of his dad bragging about the abandoned warehouse down by the river, the things they'd done to people there. It had gone to ruin, his dad said. About to crumble. Too risky to go there now. Even the police didn't bother. Nigel laughs aloud like a lunatic as he kicks open the door. Inside, he stands on top of a pile of bricks and looks around. This is better than he'd imagined. He's struck gold. It's pretty impressive, he has to admit, what the Watsons have managed to do with the place. He puts on the headphones, presses Play. It takes a second for the music to infect him and when it does, his mind scrambles the original plan and designs something infinitely more fun instead. What can he say? This appetite for destruction, it's in his blood.

"Where the hell is he?" Sid can't settle. He has already run through every worst-case scenario. Nigel murdered by the Watsons. Nigel lying dead on the distillery floor, the victim of some freak accident. Nigel dobbing them into the police, just because he can.

"You're such a drama queen. I'm sure he's fine." Scott bounces his ball on the table top. It's nearly closing time. Nigel should have been back an hour ago.

Nigel knows this pub like his own front room. He's been coming here for years. He squeezes in through the goods entrance at the back, helps himself to a packet of Scampi Fries. He spots Scott and Sid a mile off. They're drinking juice, sitting there shitting themselves with fear, looking out the window like a couple of orphans. He wonders what the deal is with the two of them, who's gonna make the first move. Elliott, he reckons. Sadowskyj doesn't have it in him.

Nigel can't resist. "Boo," he whispers. Watching them both jump out of their skins sends a twinge of pure joy through his nerves. Sometimes Nigel thinks he was born to be a sadist. He always gets a kick out of making people squirm. He muscles Sid's head into a headlock.

Scott pulls up a chair for him. "And?" he whispers.

Nigel makes himself comfortable, signals at the barman for a pint of his usual. He throws an empty matchbox onto the table and smirks. "Job done."

Scott's face drops as he puts his finger on what the smell is. Nigel's jeans are smeared in petrol. One simple fucking job and he can't even follow instructions. He has to go fucking *off piste*. "You *torched* the place?"

"Jesus, Nigel." Sid knew this would happen. He looks around to check that nobody has heard.

Nigel is indignant. What's he gonna do, go back there with the fire brigade, offer to put out the inferno? "I did a bit of exploring. You told me to use my imagination."

"We thought you'd do something small," hisses Scott. "Make a hairline crack in a pipe or something, so that it drips out slowly."

"The whole point was so they wouldn't realise straight away." Sid is livid. This better not come back to them. "You wore the gloves, right?"

A pint of Guinness appears on the table in front of Nigel.

He downs half the glass. He's earned it. He hears the sirens of a dozen fire engines screeching along the bypass. A job well done. He belches loudly. "If you'd really wanted a hairline crack, you wouldn't have called me."

"He's got a point," says Scott to Sid. "He's solved our problem overnight. We should be celebrating."

"Excuse me lads." Nigel finishes his pint, wipes his mouth on his sleeve. "No offense, but I can't be seen with you two."

"So, what's next?" asks Sid, once they're out of the pub. The Shambles is the last place Sid wants to be. They're walking quickly, the only sober people on the street. Tourist season never seems to end in York and the lane is buzzing with people out for the night, crawling from pub to wine bar and Sid wonders who has to pick up the pieces when they finally call it a night. He tries to steer clear of this part of town, finds himself instantly annoyed by the dawdling couples wearing overpriced cameras like a fashion accessory. The problem with tourists, he thinks, is that they lack imagination. Where's the art in taking a photograph of the same statue, from the same perspective, as everybody else? Sid always goes for the candid, stolen shots of people, the ever-changing landscape of everyday life. He hangs back, watches as Scott storms along the cobbles, refusing to alter his course, making couples break hands so that he can pass. He pulls the Dreamchasers list from his back pocket, jogs to catch up with his friend.

Scott stops on the bridge and turns to Sid, reading his mind. "Let's have a little fun," he says.

CHAPTER 15

"My head's wrecked," moans Sid, leaning melodramatically against a railing. "Can't we just go to school?"

"We're going, like we agreed last night." says Scott, striding ahead. "You can stay here if you want, but I'm going."

"Why is everything right this second or never with you?" Sid picks up his bag from the pavement.

"You shouldn't have had that shandy. It's not my fault you're a total featherweight."

"Yeah, yeah." Sid checks his watch. He's meant to be in physics. Mrs Collins will be tapping her spindly fingers against the blackboard. He can never understand a word she says. It's like she's speaking in code. He's glad he isn't there. Besides, the live-in carer has everything under control with his mum. For the first time in his life, Sid feels like he has a pass to do what he wants to do. Six days without anyone to care for but himself. He slams his palm against Scott's back. "Right then. Let's do this."

It's nearly midday when their train pulls into King's Cross. Businessmen on their way to boozy lunches and executives slipping home early for a long weekend navigate around Sid and Scott. In their casual clothes, they stand out a mile amongst the tweed and Italian leather of the people around them. Sid is acutely aware of feeling cheap. Of being looked at as though he doesn't belong on that stretch of pavement. For the first time in his life, Scott understands why his father had always worn a suit. Even when it was completely inappropriate. It is a means to equilibrium, a way of levelling the playing field.

Scott looks along the street in both directions, scrutinising the shop fronts and the antiquated signs. "Which one's Savile Row?" he asks.

"How should I know?" says Sid. He takes a step back into the road and is looking up at the shops when a car beeps behind him.

"Fu-cking hell!" shouts Scott in admiration. The car is a Ferrari Testarossa. Cherry red and polished to a sheen intended to be intimidating. Scott isn't intimidated. He just can't stop looking. "Alright, mate," he says, as the door opens.

A tall blonde woman, the driver, looks them up and down and swans past without a word, making the whole scene even more bizarre.

Sid grins. London isn't just the place of dreams. It is the place of his, Sid Sadowskyj's, specific down-to-the-minutest-detail-of-the-way-she-wears-her-hair dream. He watches her walk beneath red awnings that match the shade of her court shoes exactly. She glides into a shop.

Scott is still admiring the car, trying to calculate how many ovens it would take to afford this. They need a bigger plan.

"I think I've found Savile Row," says Sid, still smiling after the woman.

Sid wants to stride in confidently, like the man he hoped he would become but, when it comes down to it, he buckles under the awnings and pushes Scott ahead through the rotating front door.

Scott is in awe by the gleaming parquet floor, the rails of suits stretching into the back of the shop. There is something about the space that feels different to anywhere he's set foot in before, and it takes him a second to realise it is *wealth* that he's imbibing.

"Can I help you?"

She appears out of nowhere, polished and striking in a white shirt with sharp collars. Sid hardly recognises her. She is so in keeping with the decor of the boutique that he can't imagine her existing anywhere outside of it. It is almost impossible to equate her with the woman he'd seen in the street a minute earlier. Now that she is close up, he realises that she is unnaturally tall, towering over the pair of them. She smells of vanilla perfume tinged with the tang of multiple cigarettes. Girls like her don't exist back home.

"We're here to buy a suit. A good one," says Scott. He can tell already, from the unconvinced shape her red lips are taking, that he and Sid aren't her usual clientele. Lucky for them the shop is empty and she can't pretend that she doesn't have time for them. "We've shopped here before," Scott lies. "And my dad is an old regular of yours."

"We've travelled down from York," says Sid and immediately regrets it. He was just trying to think of something to say, but he is certain it's made him sound provincial, clueless. He's sure that she's stifling a laugh.

"Take a seat, gentlemen" she tells them. Almost as an afterthought, she picks up a catalogue and hands it to Scott. "The prices start at three thousand." She watches the boy's expression before deciding whether to continue. "That's for your standard tailored suit. That's your trousers and jacket." She crosses the room and disappears behind a velvet curtain at the back of the shop.

"I think we should leave," whispers Sid. He doesn't deserve to be in a place like this. This is the realm of politicians, film stars and royalty, not a couple of upstarts from the north. He didn't like the way she'd looked him up and down, as though taking him all in, assessing every inch.

"This is exactly what I had in mind," says Scott, engrossed in the pages. The photo could have been taken in any era: the model's hair is slicked back with pomade, and the lines of the suit are timeless, wouldn't look out of place in a Hitchcock film. Scott smiles. He could write a whole script around this guy in the catalogue.

Sid looks at Scott and, realising he's already made up his mind, resigns himself to seeing it through. "Give us a look, then," he says.

The shop assistant smiles when she sees them huddled together on the chaise-longue, fighting over the catalogue. So, they haven't done a runner after all. Which means two things: one, they can afford the products and two, she hasn't scared them off. She is well aware of how strangers viewed her. She blames her Scandinavian grandmother for a lifetime's unwarranted accusation of being a snob. OK, so she works in a shop in Mayfair, but it is a creative job and she loves the art of playing the part, getting to drive a company car that turns heads, getting dolled up in the morning. It's all part of the theatre. It allows her to kick off her heels at the end of the day and relax in a flat that affords her the lifestyle she's always dreamed of. Floor to ceiling bookcases, a two-minute cycle ride to Hampstead Heath. Fresh peonies from the florist if she turns left from her front door, and two doors down for the best chinese takeaway in London. The job is just a job. Not an extension of her personality, not a way of meeting people, but simply a means to an end. She enjoys excelling in her role, giving her customers exactly what they want. These boys are no exception. They've come to her shop to be spoiled, and she'll find a way to give them what they've come for, even if it means digging around in last season's stock for something they can take home today.

Walking along the streets of Mayfair, their old clothes folded neatly away into a new leather hold-all, they are both convinced that they have grown taller in the hour it took her to suit them up.

"She smiled at me as we were leaving," says Sid, craning to catch sight of himself in the reflective surfaces of department store windows, red telephone boxes and double decker buses.

"You just spent three grand in her store," replies Scott. "Of course she smiled at you!"

"You don't think she was flirting?"

Scott is already growing weary of the neighbourhood they've found themselves in. There is nothing down-to-earth about the designer boutiques and the women with bug-eyed sunglasses who suddenly take notice of him, who smile sweetly as he and Sid walk past. Scott can't stand that fakery.

"Nah," says Sid, still smiling. "She was definitely flirting with me."

Scott stops at a crossroads. There are signs everywhere and the streets are packed with pedestrians. His instinct is to find a quiet street and see where it leads to. He doesn't want to follow the crowds.

"What's next?" asks Sid. So far, he's been following Scott's lead, but he gets the impression that Scott is getting bored. The last thing Sid wants is to be stuck in a massive city with someone who wants to be alone. He tries to maintain the momentum, to regain some control. "More shopping?"

"We can shop anytime," mutters Scott. He has a brainwave.

Old films. Suits. He throws his hands to the sky. "We need some cigars!"

"It's like a library," says Sid, taking in the tall shelves of cigars, the ladder that hangs from a rail running the length of the shop. Instead of the spines of books, the shelves are carefully stacked with sealed wooden boxes, secure behind glass. The air feels different in here. It's all wood and smoke, like he imagines that Scout camp would have smelt like, if he'd ever been allowed to go. He takes a step further into the shop.

Scott is passing his bouncy ball from palm to palm. There's something static about this place. The second they'd walked in from the street and closed the heavy door behind them. It had given him goosebumps. Like it hasn't changed in centuries. Time tick-tocking away and everything stays the same forever. "Looks like someone died in that chair," he says. He crosses the room, settles down into the ancient leather armchair in the corner. It's less comfortable than it looks and he's up on his feet again, bouncing from boot to boot, trying to think of the most modern song he knows. He bets Olsen would love it in here.

"Hey Scott," whispers Sid. It feels like the kind of place where you should whisper. There are dozens of oil paintings on the wall, dark portraits staring him out. He's losing his nerve. Through a closed glass door, a spindly man in a three-piece suit has his back to them, engrossed in conversation with a prospective buyer. He is wearing white gloves and a pocket watch. It's all so surreal, like they've landed in Wonderland. Sid hisses a little louder to get Scott's attention. "Should we just go?"

Scott takes a leap across the black-and-white chequerboard floor towards Sid, uses his arms for balance. Lands both feet on his intended square. He wishes he could erase most of the useless crap Malcolm tried to teach him. Swipe it from his mind, just shake it clear like an Etch A Sketch, start again on a more permanent canvas. Chess, though. He hates to admit it, but chess just won't budge. There's something in it. The strategy of a good game. He winks at Sid. "Your move."

"Would you just..." Sid holds a finger to his lips. The shopkeeper is opening a box for the customer to inspect, gesturing with his spare hand as though ruminating on life. He still hasn't clocked them.

"Ah, come on," says Scott. "Live a little." He needs to throw his whole weight into his next move, aiming to make a knight's leap, two squares right and one square forwards. It's difficult in his suit. His arms feel like a marionette's. The fabric's not cut for improvised movements. He has to concentrate. For a second, he forgets he is holding his bouncy ball. He flings up his arms to launch.

The ball does its own thing. Sid realises before Scott does. He sees it all pan out, the ricochet of the ball, its trajectory, the way it will bounce once, twice, over the Persian rug and up towards the glass cube suspended from the ceiling, the cube that he can tell just by looking holds the really expensive cigars. The ones they'll never be able to afford. He looks at Scott, and it's slow motion, the pair of them lunging to intercept the ball, Scott tripping over his untied boot laces, grabbing at an immovable life-size marble statue to steady himself, Sid reaching out, diving now, at full stretch, not even thinking about the fact he's never made a decent catch in his life, mind over matter, cupping the bouncy ball before it does any damage. He lands on the rug with a dull thud.

Scott is grinning down at him, extending an arm. He raises an eyebrow, impressed.

"That was close," says Sid, closing his hand tightly around the bouncy ball. He's not getting it back. No fucking way.

"Shush," mocks Scott. Funniest thing he's seen in forever. His mind's already plotting the way they would film it, the high-angle shot from way up in the rafters, the symmetry of the cigar shop, a circle of pink pinballing around it. Sid's face. Maybe in the film he'd just let the cube smash.

They are still dusting themselves down as the shopkeeper appears. Scott laughs out loud as Sid does that thing he always does, the little dip of the head and hands clasped behind his back, his Sid-by-numbers move whenever he's in the presence of someone important.

The shopkeeper strides past them, rings up the other customer's purchase on the vintage till, holds the door open and bids him good day. He turns his attention to Scott and Sid. "Sirs?" His voice strains. From a distance, the young men had seemed part of the furniture, clothed head to toe in Savile Row, a little eccentric for their age perhaps but that's nothing unusual in a shop like this. Close up, he sees, they are utterly ridiculous. He notices the blonde one's clunky tan desert boots, the filthy soles depositing clumps of mud the length and breadth of his shop. He summons his most polite voice. "Would you mind terribly?"

"Eh?" Scott looks at him blankly.

"Your shoes, Sir." The shopkeeper points to a sign engraved in brass above the front door. "We have a policy," he says.

Scott walks up close to the sign, reads the archaic list of rules for potential customers. He pulls off his boots, tosses them towards the door.

The shopkeeper flinches.

"We'd like to buy some cigars," ventures Sid. He straightens up Scott's boots, puts them heel to heel and toe to toe, places his own shoes neatly beside them for good measure.

"I see," says the shopkeeper. He smiles despite himself. Quiet days like this, a little entertainment doesn't go amiss. The boys are an absolute shambles. It's almost endearing. They think he hasn't noticed the pink bouncy ball clenched tightly in the hand of the dark-haired lad. The little pink ball that almost obliterated fifteen grand in a heartbeat. Eyes in the back of his head. Comes with the territory. "Now usually," he says. "I go through the motions of being polite to newcomers, ever-so-nicely explain that it's best not to touch anything, gently urge the nervous beginner towards an Edicion Limitada and go home a happy man." He claps his hands together. "But let's just skip the pretense, shall we? Follow me."

Scott tries to nudge Sid, ask him what the hell is the deal with this guy, but Sid is already walking on tiptoes across the floor, obeying orders. Scott trudges behind them. Above his head, through a half-moon shaped internal window, he can see the brogues and legs of two men on the next floor up, a swirl of smoke between them.

"The smoking room," explains the shopkeeper, pointing up to the window. "Of course, that's only for regulars." He comes to a stop, gently pulls a slim wooden box from a low shelf. "So. You like Shakespeare."

Scott and Sid frown.

"The quote on your hand," the man explains, as he carefully breaks the seal on the cigar box. "Twelfth Night. Act Two, Scene Five if I'm not mistaken."

Scott inspects the back of his hand. He doesn't even remember writing it this time. It's become so automatic.

The man is appalled by the boy's handwriting, doesn't see much point on commenting on it. He takes two sealed cigars from the box, can't resist passing them under his nose to inhale. "Cohiba," he annunciates. He hands one each to Scott and Sid. "Now pay up and skedaddle."

It takes their lungs an hour to recover. They lean against the lions in Trafalgar Square, coughing so much that appalled parents appear from nowhere to rescue their kids from the plinths, glaring at Scott and Sid as they evacuate their loved ones from the smoke and splutters.

"I can't believe people smoke these things," rasps Scott, between laughing at Sid and worrying about dying.

Sid runs to the fountain, cups his hands, takes a long drink.

He wants to submerge his head under the water, Scott can tell. Give it time. Forcing Sid out of his comfort zone, it was the right move. A chance for him to shed his skin.

"I...er...made an appointment," Sid says, later, as they eat sushi from a revolving conveyer belt piled high with food they've never tried before. "While you were spending ages in the record shop."

"Didn't even notice you'd gone."

"Exactly."

"Wanna see what I got?" Scott reaches for his bag.

"Later. Scott, I'm trying to tell you something big. They had a cancellation. My appointment's at three. I already had a consultation." He pushes awkwardly at the glasses he's been wearing for as long as he can remember. "I don't want to hide anymore."

"What kind of appointment?" Scott's face contorts at the unexpected taste of wasabi. "The fuck was that?" he spits.

"To get my eyes lasered," explains Sid, as if it's nothing. He's been mulling it over for months. He pulls out a plastic folder from his bag, hands Scott a pristine driving license that states his age as nineteen.

"Where'd you get that?"

"Internet."

"Right then." Scott reaches across his friend, grabs a plate of towering sushi from the conveyor belt before it passes him by.

"Isn't it, like, major surgery?"

"Ninety-nine per cent success rate," says Sid, blocking out the one per cent. "Takes about an hour and a half, all in."

Scott is constantly surprised by Sid. Since the truth came out about his mum, Sid hasn't so much as come out of his shell as shot himself human-cannonball-style from it. He shows no sign of relenting. "Need me to come in with you?"

Sid shakes his head.

"I saw some guys under that bridge down there," says Scott between mouthfuls. "Want me to get you something to calm the…"

Sid shakes his head. "That wouldn't be helpful."

"I'm joking, mate. Shit though, you sure? Massive needle drilling into your eye? What if it's not been sterilised."

"It's a laser, Scott."

"You sure you don't want me to come with you? What if you go blind? It's not one of them back alley clinics, is it?"

"Meet you outside the record store later," says Sid, smiling, grabbing a plate of Japanese curry from the conveyor belt and putting it down in front of his friend. "I'll drop you a text when I'm done," he shouts, running for the door.

"How much did it hurt?" Scott's desperate to know the details but Sid, as usual, is playing it cool.

"Didn't." Sid nearly throws his old glasses into the bin, thinks better of it. Best not get ahead of himself. Just in case. One per cent and all that. He buries them deep in his bag.

"Less than amputation, more than toothache?" asks Scott, handing Sid the smoothie he's bought him from the stall down the road. He'd almost asked for a couple of slices of cucumber for Sid's eyes, wasn't sure of the etiquette. He'd seen his mum do that, the cucumber on the eyelids thing, heard her say it was soothing. "Can I just…" Scott is poking at Sid's giant prescription black sunglasses. "Very superstitious…" he begins to sing.

"Eh?" Sid swipes Scott's hand away. "Leave it!"

Scott never ceases to be amazed by Sid's complete lack of knowledge about pop culture. Give the lad a page of algebra and he's happy for days, but a reference to music? Nothing. Zilch. Not even a giggle.

"What's next then?" asks Sid. They've been powering through the list, hardly stopping for breath. Suited, booted, fed and lasered, there is only one thing left on today's dreamchasing agenda. Sex with girl. They can't put it off any longer.

"You sure you're alright?"

Sid takes off his sunglasses for a moment, catches sight of his new reflection in the glass of a shopfront, almost doesn't recognise himself. "Never better."

Sid stares around The King's Arms and tries desperately to like it. He folds up the sunglasses and squints in the bright room.

Scott wants to feel at home here, but everything about the place makes him feel ill at ease. The colours are all wrong. Nothing matches. There is a peculiar smell, somewhere between puke and tobacco, that was never conveyed in the pubs on telly; you didn't catch the cast of Eastenders holding their noses as they walked into The Queen Vic. He looks at the carpet. He can tell that once, maybe a couple of decades ago, a pattern like this would have been the height of fashion, all orange and brown. It is the same with the wallpaper: green in some places, red flocked in others and bare plaster around the dart board. There are all sorts. As though all the misfits and miscreants have been scraped together off the London streets against their will. Still wary of each other, they perch on mismatched stools, lean on tables, try to outsmart each other over the sound of the jukebox.

The barmaid eyes Scott and Sid suspiciously. Young men in suits are always a cause for concern. They almost always mean drugs or religion. She doesn't have the patience to deal with the fallout of either. Drugs she could turn a blind eye to, but there is no space at her bar for preachers. They are walking over. She slings the glass-cleaning cloth over her shoulder and braces herself. "Yep?" she says, bored of them already.

Scott wonders what her problem is. They're in a bar. She is a barmaid. It isn't rocket science. He wants a drink.

Sid smiles at the woman, silently studying the bottles behind the bar, wondering how to pronounce 'Laphroaig'. It both repulses and fascinates him, the world of drinking. The extremes it brings out in people. Aside from his mum, he's seen grown men cry and sane people act like maniacs, all because of a glass or two.

"Two vodka martinis, shaken not stirred." Scott smiles as he says it.

The barmaid pulls her lanky hair into a ponytail and emits a shrill shriek. Behind the bar, the china plate depicting the coronation of Queen Elizabeth rattles on its shelf. The barmaid's face sets back to a glum stone cast. She stares humourlessly at the boys. "You taking the piss?"

Sid shrinks a little into his new shoes and counts the whisky bottles. He is aware that the old guys on the nearest table have turned around to get a look at the newcomers. He thought pubs were meant to friendly places. To him, the whole place feels like a distant relative's sitting room after a will has been read, full of grudges and borderline conflict. "Coke, please," he says to the barmaid.

"Orange juice," says Scott.

Without taking her eyes off the pair of them, the barmaid fills two half-pint glasses and plonks them on the bar. The drinks slop onto the already-sopping mats on the bar. "Five twenny," she snaps.

Scott hands her a ten pound note.

"You buying me a drink?" she asks.

Scott passes the Coke to Sid, who sips it immediately, so that he doesn't have to join in the conversation. He can feel Scott's blood boiling from here.

Sid glances again at the table nearby. Yep, he wasn't imagining it. The girls are still making eye contact with him. Feeling bold, he takes a gamble and raises his glass to them like he's seen men do in the movies. The girls nudge each other and smile. Sid stands mesmerised. He hadn't expected that reaction. Maybe this place isn't so hostile after all. He turns back to Scott. God, he's a nightmare sometimes. Even a simple transaction in a bar turns into a hostage situation. It's a strange thing. In many respects, Scott is an introvert. He spends hours alone, reading. He'd rather live in a film than the real world. But, when it comes to confrontation, Scott never thinks twice.

Scott grins at the barmaid and the change on her face is immediate. The lines on her mouth, downturned from a life of cynicism, disappear. She smiles back at him and repeats her question. "So, *are* you buying me a drink?"

"No," says Scott, his voice blunt. That's another thing that Sid has noticed about his friend. At times, Scott is capable of absolute cruelty. Scott lays out his palm and waits for his change.

She slams the till shut and unceremoniously deposits his coins on the bar.

Everything in London feels too big for Scott, too brash. There are too many potential enemies. "Thanks," he says to the barmaid, to show there are no hard feelings.

They slurp their drinks through their straws.

"It just says sex with girls," says Sid, squinting to read the list.

"We find out as much as possible about them," instructs Scott.

"What about..." Sid whispers. "The sex?" It had been a while since he and Scott had sat up on the hill and first talked about girls. Sid had admitted to being a virgin, that he'd never even held hands with a girl and Scott had promised to change all that. He'd been less forthcoming about his own experiences, leading Sid to wonder what the story was. But now, it seemed like it was now or never. Sid was ready. He wanted a kiss at least. No harm in positive thinking.

Scott is appalled. "What, in here?"

"Back at their place."

"What if it smells? Their place." Scott rubs at his temple, imagining filth. For all his messiness, he can't stand the thought of being forced into a shitty house. He can see it already. Mouldy plates beneath the bed that he'll catch sight of as he is lying down with her. A pillow with bed bugs crawling all over it.

"Why would it?"

"I dunno but... can't do it."

Sid glances again at the table. The two women are still looking. "Let's just see if they'll even let us sit down first." He sidles over. "'Scuse me, do you mind if we sit down?"

The blonde woman is quick to answer. "Yes," she mocks. "I do."

Sid slinks away, mortified.

"Grab a seat," she bellows. "What's with the drinks?"

Sid sits down. They look like the kind of girls his mum used to warn him about, back in the days when she could still be bothered to impart any of her wisdom to her son.

"You Jehovah's Witnesses?" asks her friend, moving her feet from the seat so that Scott can sit opposite her.

"No. We're cleaners."

Scott throws his jacket over a nearby chair and rolls his sleeves up as he sits down. He feels like a dick in the suit. He'd only bought it out of a sense of necessity. Sid looks awesome in his, but Scott can't get used to the way the fabric itches against his neck. He can hardly move in it. The pockets are sewn up so there's nowhere to put anything. It's just not his style.

The table between them is etched with a dozen different names scored coarsely into the wood.

Sid's girl, who introduces herself as Jade, has the kind of cover girl hair that only someone with time on their hands and a desire to be adored would slave to achieve. Tara, the girl opposite Scott, is wearing shimmery lip gloss that makes her lips glisten like a licked lollipop. Scott hopes that she is the quiet one. He's not in the mood for small talk. He just wants to get on with it.

"Did she give you a hard time?" Jade nods towards the barmaid.

"Something like that," says Sid.

Tara takes a swig from her bottle. "She don't like suits," she says. "We think she had a bad experience with a lawyer or something."

"Got her back up."

The girls laugh.

Scott and Sid laugh, too. This chatting-to-girls thing is easier than they'd been led to believe. Scott looks around the pub. There are plenty of other young guys about. The lads playing pool wear football tops. A couple of old-school punks sit on the next table along, skinheads with braces and red Docs. Scott knows better than to stare. But he's a little jealous. He'd kill to be wearing his ripped army pants right now, some worn-thin T-shirt and his favourite boots. He has nothing to lose. He goes for the kill. "So, what makes you orgasm?"

Sid spits out his orange juice. He wipes at his mouth with his hand and hopes the girls haven't noticed. He is fine. They are both staring at Scott. Scott is giving them one of his prize smiles. Sid does the same. He'd been told he had a nice smile, once. He hopes to God it will do the trick.

"Well, err," begins Tara, uncertain whether this is a wind-up. Boys are never this direct. She half expects someone to jump out with a video camera. What the hell, she might as well act the part. "I've never had one from my, a guy."

"How come?" asks Scott, putting his elbows on the table and leaning forward to listen. The weirder he can seem, the better Sid will look. He's seen it in films. A kind of good cop bad cop routine, a wing-man if you like, that never failed to work. Sid needs all the help he can get.

"They've just never done it!"

"So you've never had an orgasm?"

The four of them are engrossed in the conversation, their heads bowed close across the table, an intense cocoon amidst the growing clamour of the pub.

"No, I have," says Tara. It's funny. She doesn't feel weird talking about sex with these boys. It's like their obvious virginity makes them neutral somehow. The boys seem to have a weird bond that borders on brotherhood. "I have," she continues, "but only by doing it my special way."

Sid wriggles a little in his seat. He has all kinds of images flashing through his mind. He can't believe that Scott is keeping it together so well.

"Why not by a boy?" asks Scott, with the joyous, fearful curiosity of a nature journalist swimming with orcas.

"Guys just want to screw you!" says Jade.

"Amen to that," agrees Tara.

Scott and Sid sit back in their seats. For Sid, listening to the girls is like being struck by lightning, each bolt stronger than the last. He wishes he could write it all down. There is no way he'll remember everything.

"It hurts after a while," says Jade.

Sid nods. He can't think of anything to say.

"What does?" asks Scott, keeping up his act.

"It just gets irritating," says Tara.

"Did you tell them?"

"No," says Tara.

"No way," says Jade.

"Do they know?" he pushes.

"What?"

"That you don't orgasm?"

"Probably," says Jade.

Sid doesn't get it. If it was so unenjoyable, why not just say something. "Why don't you tell them what to do? Or ask them to do it differently?"

Jade had never thought of it like that. When it comes down to the act, there is never much time for discussion. "My last boyfriend was supposed to be some sex god."

"Oh god, him..." remembers Tara.

Jade laughs at the thought of him. "He went down on me and we could play around for hours but... I still never came. He just stuck it in, lasted five minutes. Then acted like I should be so thankful."

"So... what's your special thing?" Sid asks.

"Special thing?"

Scott smiles. Now you're talking, Sid. His plan has worked. Sidney Sadowskyj is finally asking the questions.

Sid can feel his cheeks burning. He wishes he'd stayed quiet. "To make yourself, you know, get excited and all?"

Tara smiles. "I'll have to show you sometime."

"Me too," says Jade.

Sid's blush deepens as the girls giggle. He glances across at Scott. Scott is watching them intently, with the same expression on his face as when he watches a film for the first time, trying to remember the lines.

"So..." teases Tara. "You already made one mistake."

Scott takes a sip of his juice and frowns. There'd been no mistakes. His pitch had been perfect. It was just a matter of time before Sid was thanking him for a job well done. "What's that, then?"

"Where's our drinks?" asks Jade. She holds up her empty bottle.

Sid looks blankly at her. Call it naivety, but his mind can't keep up. One minute they're talking about how to orgasm, the next they've moved onto completely mundane matters. Sid's mind is still on Jade's offer to show him her special method.

"You'd better get them," says Scott. "I think the barmaid hates me." He punches Sid in the ribs to jolt him out of his thoughts.

"Yeah, sure," says Sid. He doesn't want to move. He'd always been pretty good at controlling himself, you know, down there, but he's only human. He takes a deep breath and slides out of his seat. He takes off his suit jacket and holds it in front of his waist. "Erm, what would you like?"

"Surprise us," says Tara.

"Right." Sid disappears into the crowd. He comes back a second later. "Can I borrow some money?" his whispers into Scott's ear.

"I left the change on the bar. So," he turns his attention back to the women. He steps up his PR campaign for Sid. "He's an enigma," he says, nodding towards Sid at the bar.

Jade glances over to the skinny boy at the bar. Sid is struggling to get served, far too polite amongst the other men shouting their orders. She feels sorry for him. "He seems kinda closed."

The whole Eastwood thing, Scott thinks. Sid's definitely got that going for him. Scott leans forward and speaks quietly to add gravitas to his next statement. "Still waters run deep."

Jade smiles and pulls a pot of lip gloss from her handbag. She and Tara dip their index fingers into the pot and smear the gloss onto their lips.

"You want some?" asks Jade, offering it to Scott.

At the same time, Tara's foot searches beneath the table for Scott's groin. Her stiletto falls to the floor with a clack as she presses the arch of her foot against him.

"What? No!" says Scott, slightly offended at having been asked. He shifts back in his chair, so that Tara's foot can't quite reach. He is thankful when Sid returns.

"Ta," says Jade. The drink looks exciting. Bright yellow with a pink straw. A paper umbrella bobs on the top. "What is it?"

"Pineapple juice," says Sid.

"And what else?"

"Ice," says Sid, passing an orange juice to Scott.

Jade laughs loudly and leans over to Sid. He looks so uncomfortable, she thinks. She drops her straw in his glass and takes a sip of his drink. "You're the cute one," she says, smiling.

Sid doesn't know what to say. Girls are never this forward. He's learned everything he knows about women over the past few weeks, sitting in Scott's bedroom watching carefully-selected movies. Scott seems determined to give Sid an education that school cannot offer. In films, there are usually a whole lot more games before the leg-stroking stage. But, no, it seems that Jade has watched different films to Sid. She is leaning forward so that her breasts rest on the table and her hand is creeping up the inside of his leg. "Nice pineapple juice?" he stutters.

"You know." Jade walks her fingernails up along the inside of his thigh, looking for a way in. "Pineapple juice is supposed to make your cum taste nice."

"Really," says Sid, hoping that he sounds seductive. "I'll have to try that sometime."

Tara pulls a face.

Scott is laughing at Sid. He checks his watch. He's got them tickets for a gig at the Albert Hall, some young composer. Even blagged tickets to the afterparty. Their first night in London and he's done with time-wasting, ticking off boxes. Time to go. "So. You ready to Bob Dylan it?" he asks Sid.

Sid flashes him a look. Scott has this real knack for bad timing. Here they are. There'd been no kissing, but they were past first base for sure. Surely? And now Scott wants to leave. "Er." He tries to get his feelings across in the tone of his voice. "Sure?"

"Bob Dylan it?" asks Tara.

"Rolling stone, no moss, etc. etc." Scott's voice is terse. He's bored of this now. Sid seems to be moving at the pace of a snail. They've had their fun. It's time to go. He puts on his jacket. "We've got some things we have to do."

Tara sits back in her seat, unimpressed. Bloody men. They're all the same. Pretending to be interested, spending all this time chatting you up, and then what. All for nothing. They probably had to get home to their girlfriends.

Jade's fingers reach the zip on Sid's trousers. "I just need ten minutes," she says, smiling at him. "Fancy joining me to the loo?"

"Yeah!" says Sid eagerly. "I mean, sure, whatever." He smiles nervously as she takes his hand. Tara and Scott stand up to let him past, both refusing to hide their disinterest.

Jade leads Sid through a maze of corridors.

He watches the way she walks, still not really believing that it is happening. It is as though every movement is calculated to affect him. The way she struts one leg in front of the other. The way the black line on the back of her tights makes him wonder what is at the top of them. The smell of her hair. Sid has the feeling she's done this before. She bolts the lock behind them. Sid looks around, wishes he hadn't. She slams him up against the door. The glass is transparent except for the big black lettering that says "Disabled", but she doesn't care who is looking. Besides, no one ever comes down here. She presses her hips against his and gives him a deep kiss.

"Do..." Sid pushes her gently away.

Jade wraps her hands around his neck and kisses him again.

He wriggles free and smiles nervously at her. This wasn't exactly what he'd had in mind. "Do you want to get a room?"

She steps back and turns around. She smiles to herself. This move always works. She looks at him over her shoulder. So what if there is no music. She can hear it in her head, and she begins to unbutton her blouse, slowly, one button at a time, pushing her chest out so that the fabric stretches to its limits. She watches him the whole time. She can always tell when they like it.

Sid watches as she twirls around on the carpet and throws her blouse on the floor. "There's probably wee on the floor, you might want to hang..." he begins.

Jade shrieks with laughter and dances towards him. She'd felt him get hard ages ago, sat at the table. He's waited long enough. She wants him. She looks in his eyes. He is nervous, she can tell. It's always the quiet ones you have to watch. He's gentle. Not like his friend. Scott was all talk. She bet that Sid was going to take her to places she'd never been before. She pulls her skirt up and reaches for his hands.

With his hands on her waist, Sid wonders how long he should wait before he reaches down between her legs. She is warm down there, he can tell already. It looks like she wants to touch him first. She is unbuckling his belt. Sid looks up and quickly shut his eyes again. She is rubbing him. Oh Jesus, he's spent three years trying to build up the guts to make a move on Lucy at school and now this girl, that he's only just met, is touching him there. His body jolts on the spot. It feels good.

She bites his neck. "This is going to be…" she begins.

Sid scrunches up his eyes. It feels too good.

Jade's jaw is slack, her eyes narrowed. "You're joking, right?"

Sid smiles as his body relaxes. He opens his eyes. "You're so good at that," he says.

Jade squeals, jumps back, runs to the sink and holds her hand under the tap for an insultingly long time.

Sid tries to catch his breath. "That was ace! Do you want me to… hey," he says, as Jade picks up her clothes and storms out of the toilet, slamming the door behind her. He wonders what he did wrong. He thought they were just getting started.

Scott and Tara sit as far away from each other as possible, Scott on the edge of his seat and Tara slumped against the wall. He watches as she carves her name into the table, and wonders whether it is uncomfortable to have such long nails. He doesn't bother asking. Scott glances around the room. The pub is still full, but none of the faces look familiar. He wonders how long they've been in here. Time seems to have warped away from them today. Maybe this was how it worked in a big city like London. People rotated. Went to work, went to the pub, went home. There were plenty of people to stand in for them whenever they were absent. Like the city never slept. It appealed to Scott. He wanted to see how it worked on an even bigger scale. Whether New York really is a city that never sleeps. Tokyo. Shanghai. He wants out of the mundane. He excuses himself.

The toilets are the kind of place where, in Hollywood films, bad things happen to good people. The Amish kid in 'Witness'. The end of Vincent in 'Pulp Fiction'. The broken toilet in 'Dumb and Dumber'. The walls are covered in phone numbers and graffiti and Scott is disgusted by the thought that'd you'd have to get right down, nose to the floor, to write some of the messages. He walks to the furthest cubicle and taps open the door with his foot.

He mutters a quiet thanks to his mum for teaching him the toilet paper trick. He'd never forgotten that holiday she'd taken him on, just after his dad left the first time, the stench of the service station toilets and the way Elaine was so patient with him even though she had tears in her eyes for most of the trip. He places the sheets all over the filthy enamel, unzips his fly and sits down. The hems of his suit are dangerously close to the floor. He holds up the fabric.

It happens. Of course it happens. Of all the disgusting toilets in the worst pubs in London, someone had to walk into this one. Scott freezes. He slides his foot along the floor to hold the door closed. The man bashes open the cubicle door next to him and unzips.

Scott sees the man's jeans drop to the floor. The old belt buckle slams on the tiles and creeps over to Scott's cubicle. He tilts his head to read the words embossed on the metal. *Harley Davidson*. The man farts loudly. Scott scrunches up his eyes. As Scott waits for the stench to come, the man speaks.

"How are you?"

Scott is horrified. "Eh, I'm... OK?"

"What are you up to?" asks the truck driver.

Scott looks at the wall between them. He wonders, if push comes to shove, whether he could quietly wriggle under the cubicle door and escape. "Er, I'm just vis..."

The man interrupts. "What are you doing tonight?"

"Ummmm..."

"Do you fancy meeting up?"

"Oh. Er no, not really. Er, this is a little awkward."

There is a long pause. Scott senses the truck driver's face turning towards his through the cubicle wall.

"Hold on love," the man says. "I've got some nutter talking to me in the toilet next to me!"

Scott's face contorts as he realises. Frozen to the spot, afraid to move an inch, he wishes the bowl could swallow him whole. *Who does that?* he thinks. Makes a phone call to his girlfriend while taking a dump?

The trousers disappear quickly as the man hoists them up. He bashes his fist against the wall of Scott's cubicle. "Freak," he growls, before rushing out of the toilet.

Scott hears the doors slamming throughout the corridor. He counts to ten, tentatively opens the cubicle door and peeps around the corner.

Sid appears after a minute. He puts his arm around Scott's shoulder and breathes out.

"So. I take it we can cross that off the list, then?" asks Scott.

"You bet," says Sid. He'd always thought that when the time came, he'd play it cool, but he just wants to scream. He can't stop smiling. It's as though a weight has been lifted from his shoulders. It is one step closer towards being normal.

Five days later, striding across the city towards King's Cross, Scott and Sid walk with a newfound swagger, their steps in unison, passing the baton of conversation back and forth from talk of parties to gigs and restaurants and near-misses and sleepless nights, wondering how they will ever come down from it all. Back to reality tomorrow.

"Can't we just stay a little longer, get a taxi home?" asks Sid. In the excitement of the last day, Sid hadn't even considered how they planned to get home. But there is no harm in having a little fun. This is the trip of a lifetime. Of his lifetime, at least. Sid isn't ready to leave just yet.

"Have you got a spare five hundred quid on you?" asks Scott.

Sid shakes his head. "I thought you had it covered."

Scott frowns. "Fifty-fifty, remember?"

There's a kid squatting in a doorway at the start of the ramp up to the station concourse. Scott gives him a cursory glance and walks on up towards the trains.

Sid stares at the boy. He can't be older than eleven. The thin cardboard he is sitting on is soaking. He isn't wearing socks. They'd seen dozens of people sleeping rough in the capital, but this was the only kid who didn't seem to be asking for money. Sid rummages in his bag for his camera. He's not sure why, but he wants to remember this moment. As a reminder to Sid to keep moving forward, to never go back. He releases the shutter just as the boy looks up. "Sorry," says Sid impulsively. The boy's stare goes right through him. Feeling suddenly guilty, Sid throws a twenty pound note towards him and jogs away.

The last train to York is in five minutes. If they run, they'll make it, easy. "I'll get the tickets," says Sid, pulling out his wallet and crossing the concourse.

"First class," says Scott. He is staring up at the departures board. The yellow pins have turned mainly to black. Theirs is the last train of the night heading north. In ten minutes, the place will be deserted. He wonders what happens when the lights go out. He bets it isn't the kind of place you want to find yourself after dark. His voice echoes across the concourse. "I'll be back!" he shouts to Sid.

The run down the ramp leaves him out of breath. He stands over the homeless boy, sweating. "Kid," he says. "You awake?"

The boy clenches his fists beneath his blanket and looks up. He was looked at by a hundred people every evening - glared at, spat at - but this guy had been different. It wasn't *pity* that the boy had seen in Scott's eyes in that split second when he'd passed a few minutes ago, and that put him in the top 1% of the population. It makes him worthy of some time now.

Scott crouches by his side and holds out his hand. "I'm Scott," he says.

The boy stares at him.

"If it was money you wanted, you'd be gone by now," Scott says. "My mate gave you money, right. What was it, ten?"

The boy looks at him blankly.

"Twenty?" asks Scott.

The boy nods.

"Listen," says Scott. "I don't want to preach but. I had to come back. You know there's another way. You always have choices." He scratches at his temple. The boy's blanket is a good one, proper thick wool, as though he'd taken it from a place where he'd once been loved. Scott thinks about his own home, how difficult it can be just to co-exist. "I figured it out," says Scott. He is speaking too quickly. Looking into the boy's eyes, the same slate grey as the smog-stained buildings nearby, Scott can't formulate his thoughts into words. "Dream!" he blurts out suddenly. "You can make your own money." He is rambling now. "Me and Sid," he gestures back towards the station. "A month ago, we had nothing... hey...no, come on, don't go."

The boy is on his feet, well accustomed to quick departures, wrapping the blanket around his shoulders like a cape.

Scott follows him down the street.

The boy is walking quickly, his eyes darting side to side. He sticks to the shadows. He's heard it all before. The kindness of strangers. It had taken him weeks to find that spot, somewhere busy enough to be safe, to hide himself in plain view. Jesus! The footsteps behind him are getting louder. He spins around. "Can you just!" He lowers his voice and stares into the stranger's blue eyes. Fancy suit and a mouthful of goodwill and he just didn't get it. "I don't have..." he wants to say that he hadn't been born with a silver spoon in his mouth, but somehow he didn't think that Scott would accept that as an excuse. "I don't have whatever it is that's made you successful." He clasps his blanket tighter around his neck. "I'm out of fight for now. I don't have any dreams left to chase. And you can tell your friend to *ask* before he takes a photograph, next time."

Scott watches him walk away until his figure becomes a silhouette against the red neon of the strip clubs. "Fuck!" he shouts, wanting to punch the brick wall, just to feel something other than crippling failure.

Sid is waiting for him at the end of the street. From his silence, Scott knows that he has seen everything.

"I was looking for somewhere to take a piss," Scott lies.

"We missed the train," says Sid. He holds up his hands, defeated. The next move is Scott's. The buoyancy Sid had felt from the night's encounters had dissipated the second he'd seen Scott sitting with the boy. Sid is over London. He wants his bed. He wants his mum.

Scott sighs loudly. "Last bus has already gone, too. Let's find a hotel," he suggests. "We can see if there's any good films on. You can choose. How much money have you got left?"

"Eighty-nine pounds, fifty-two pence," replies Sid, not having to check. That was one good thing about growing up with nothing: you always knew exactly how much you were worth at any given time.

Looking around, Scott can see signs for hotels all around them. Four stars, three stars, one star; they can have their pick. He smiles at Sid. "Hey, you said you wished you could stay longer. You win."

Sid slumps down against a bollard, not caring if his suit gets ruined. Suddenly, the extent of what he has done hits him. It doesn't feel like winning. It feels like he is about to lose everything. "I need to get home tonight." He holds his head in his hands, feeling like the worst son in the world for taking a holiday when she needed him most. Having a carer there isn't the same as having your son. It shouldn't be someone who's *paid* to give a shit. His whole life, no matter how hard things had got, how stifling the house, how fucked up the situation, Sid had always been there for her. So what if she forgot his birthday. She isn't well. She needs him. "We're screwed," he says quietly into the gutter.

"Come on, mate, it's not that bad. We can call your mum, make up some excuse. We can get the first train home tomorrow."

Sid rubs at the corners of his eyes. "I was joking about staying longer. I mean, shit, I'd love to but. I said I'd take her to her check-up tomorrow. I promised my mum. I need to keep my promises these days." He kicks at the pavement. "Is there no other way?"

Scott digs deep into his repertoire of film knowledge and comes up with an idea. "We could hitch-hike?" he suggests.

"And get murdered by some psycho and ditched somewhere near Coventry? No thanks."

Scott refuses to be defeated. "OK," he says. "Here's what we're gonna do. "I'm gonna find someone to sell this suit to..."

"But you just..."

"It's fine, it's not really my kinda thing. I can get another one when we get back to York."

Sid looks up. "Then what?"

"We can't afford a taxi so we're gonna improvise. We're gonna find a main road and we're gonna stick out our thumbs and hope and pray that it isn't a serial killer who stops." He flashes Sid a smile. "Because, this isn't a film. And seriously, what're the chances. And we're gonna pay them to take us as far as they can. And we're gonna keep on doing that until we get back to York and we drop you off on your front doorstep in time for your mum's appointment. OK?" He holds out his hands for Sid to take.

Sid allows himself to be pulled onto his feet and reluctantly agrees. The alternative scenario is too terrifying to contemplate. He can't let her down again. He can't risk it.

"It's usually the hitchhikers who are the murderers anyway." Scott smiles wickedly at Sid. "But, you know, just in case... what do you want written on your headstone?"

"Nah, y'know, I don't really think about things like that." Sid manages a smile. "Besides, I fully intend to stay alive. What would be written on yours?"

Scott spots the tail-lights of a busy road a few streets along. "I dunno. Whatever makes other people feel better when they're visiting it. Let's make a deal, Sid. If we survive this, you get to choose what's next on the list."

"Yeah, sure, thanks very much Scott. That sounds like a fair trade-off for risking my life for you." He laughs. "Party planning."

"You got a taste for it? That one on the boat in Greenwich. Like the best parts of every film I've ever seen." He runs his finger over the intricate tattoo between his thumb and forefinger, a permanent reminder of that night. "Party planning it is then."

Sid sticks his arm out into the road, thumb up, aims for a friendly-but-don't-fuck-with-me expression. "Let's do this."

"Here goes nothing."

CHAPTER 16

It's daytime in the back alley. They could scream for help. But their feet are a foot off the ground and they're gasping for air. Sid presses his palms against the brick wall as Nicky Watson leans in closer.

Nicky's breath reeks of a lifetime's tobacco. "I will find out," he leers. "And when I do, somebody is gonna be very fucking sorry."

It's impossible for Sid to retreat any further against the wall. To his left, Scott is squirming under the grip of Gavin Watson. They both hope to God this goes to plan. Their carefree days in London already feel like a lifetime ago. "Why would we have anything to do with it?" Sid manages to say.

"Ah you wouldn't," spits Nicky. "That's why I haven't burned your fuckin' eyes out."

"So why are we getting choked?" rasps Scott.

Gavin stares at Scott with absolute disdain. He's never liked the little prick, not since the first time he set eyes on him. With his airs and graces, strutting around like the world owes him something. Gavin would tear Scott to shreds in a heartbeat if his brother would let him. He tightens his grip on Scott's throat. "Sends a little message, you fuck. If somebody decides to talk, we'll find out."

"And when we do..." begins Nicky.

"... OK, OK, OK." Sid plays dumb. "When will we get more stuff then?"

"I'll let you know."

Without missing a beat, Scott delivers his line. They'd had a great time scripting this. He just hadn't expected it to feel so... real. The pain bit, the fear for his life, the hatred in the Watson Brothers' eyes, none of that was acting. His voice sounds uncharacteristically weak. "What if someone else fills the gap?"

Nicky is caught off guard. "What?"

"I mean," continues Scott, "you've created a market but if you can't service it then, I mean..."

Gavin's heard enough. His eyes narrow. His knee finds Scott's stomach in a second, his hand slamming his head against the bricks. The boy groans.

Nicky flashes his brother a cautionary stare. They're only school kids. This isn't Belfast. Easy does it. "Hold on. What are you saying?"

Sid tries to disguise his terror. He can hear Scott wheezing, struggling to recover from the blow. "W-w-what he's trying to say is... if you lose your patch, then your customers will be taken on by someone else then you'll never get them back."

"No they won't." Gavin is indignant.

"They will." Nicky can't believe his brother's stupidity sometimes. Much as he hates to admit it, the little shits are right. They can't risk it. He turns to Sid. "How many you got left?"

"Me? Erm... nothing." He makes it look as though he's thinking on his feet. "But I've got a customer who's got loads left and I could ask him if he could sell us some back."

"Aye." The Watson Brothers are united again, relieved to have a plan. "You fuckin' do that."

Nicky pats Sid on the cheek as he leaves and, despite his fear, Sid is impressed to notice that Nicky's cigarette has stayed alight throughout it all. The Watson Brothers are pros. Stumbling, bumbling, gullible pros but hey, Sid thinks, credit where credit's due. They watch them hulk away along the alley.

Scott and Sid stand paralysed against the wall, catching their breath.

"Well," chirps Scott. "Better than expected."

"Yeah."

"Ready?"

They hobble down the lane together.

"So how much do we sell it back to them for?" asks Scott. "Five quid a bottle?"

"Six," says Sid. "Two crates at a time, six quid a bottle."

"What you gonna do with the garage when it's empty? All that space."

"I'm gonna lock it up and throw away the key. Never wanna set foot in there again."

Scott throws his arm around his mate's shoulder, ignoring the pain. "Cheer up, mate." He grins. "We got away with it."

Mr Olsen makes a personal effort to venture down into the playground on this rare occasion. He spots the Elliott boy in a far corner, surrounded by a gang of admirers. They are all dancing like idiots. The boys seem to have subverted the unspoken rules of the playground. It's an odd little posse. Even Nigel Ball is there. Olsen is appalled to see that the other lad, Sadowskyj, his secret ticket to Oxbridge, is at the centre of the action.

"You're hard men to track down," he shouts.

The dancing stops.

He singles out Sid and Scott. "I've been looking for you two for the past week and a half."

Scott opens his mouth to speak.

"No excuses!" screams Olsen, his anger seething out of nowhere. "My office. Now."

Back in his room, Olsen regains his composure. He had never understood those teachers who shouted constantly. It was far more effective to use anger sparingly. It was the only way to get the attention of delinquents like the one standing in front of him now. He turns to Sidney first. The poor boy is quaking in his boots. He puts him out of his misery.

"Sidney. Thirty-two per cent attendance rate over the past term. Looking at the two of you, I can only assume that this pathetic attempt at getting yourself an education, after years of being a model student, correlates with the sudden arrival of our friend, Mr Elliott. Am I right?"

Sid stares at his knees.

"I am deeply disappointed in the both of you. Sidney, I had expected that your grades would be high enough for you to choose any university in the country. Oxbridge material if you knuckled down."

Sid's cheeks redden.

Mr Olsen turns his attention to Scott. The boy is staring straight at him with something like hatred in his eyes. "As for you, young man. It's obvious to all why you have been expelled from four previous schools. You are an appalling influence. Disruptive and a distraction in any class you deign to grace with your presence. Given that you have not only jeopardised your own future by skipping so much school and galavanting off to London..."

Scott looks surprised.

"...Yes," continues Olsen. "We have our sources. London and

God knows where, doing God knows what... but you have also made a sizeable dent in Sidney's prospects. I have no option but to expel you."

Scott is horrified, but holds his nerve.

Mr Olsen stares at him, waiting for a suitable response. Remorse. Contrition. Sometimes they beg. "Well? Have you nothing to say?"

Clenching his fists behind his back, Scott hides his anger from Olsen. "How long's this gonna take?"

It takes the headmaster a second to process Scott's response. "What?"

"I mean, you've done me a favour. I've got more important things to do."

Stunned by the cheek of him, Olsen shakes his head. This generation is all the same. An answer for everything. "My goodness, how much you have to learn. Your parents will be informed and you will attend until Friday."

Sid struggles to hold back the tears, not sure who he wants to scream at more, Scott or Olsen. He can't believe it is ending like this.

"Get out."

Scott doesn't have to be told twice.

Once they are alone, Mr Olsen chooses his words carefully. "Sid, you are a good student. But you came very close to throwing away your education."

Sid looks down again. He can hear Scott bouncing his ball outside in the corridor.

"I won't be so lenient again," warns Olsen. "I suggest that you get back to your studies. Don't be led by a fool, Sidney. Life is not a game."

Sid nods, robotically.

"Go on." Olsen finally lets him go.

Scott is nonchalant. "Ah well," he says, throwing his ball against the metal lockers. "I suppose it had to happen sometime. What did he say to you?"

Sid walks quickly, desperate to put distance between him and Scott. It's bad enough that he's being abandoned. Not only that, but Olsen's put doubts in his head about Scott, his best friend. Everything that has happened this year, made him doubt the only person who's ever made him feel good about himself. Sid doesn't know what to think anymore. He needs some time to process what has happened. "Not much," he lies. The first chance he gets, he ducks out of a fire escape without saying bye, a route he hasn't used in ages. He no longer feels like he belongs anywhere.

CHAPTER 17

Even home feels like a foreign country. Approaching his house, Sid is nervous. He stands at the back door, wondering whether to knock. The light is on in the kitchen, and he can hear music. He holds up his fist to knock, then thinks better of it. This is still his home.

As he turns his key in the lock, Sid notices the new plant pot on the outside sill. The soil is damp from the recent rain, and there is a tiny green stem sprouting from the dirt. It's a positive omen.

"Hello?" he shouts, louder than necessary, not wanting to startle her. He looks around the kitchen and his heart sinks. They had a deal. Mondays were her turn to do the washing up. Sid sighs. The surfaces are covered in dirty plates. His mum has abandoned her one-set policy, and it seems that every item they own has been used. Sid can't help himself. He dumps his bag on the kitchen floor and sets about gathering up the dirty dishes.

"What you playing at, son?"

Sid spins around. His mum is wearing a baggy purple jumper over stretchy red jeans. It is the first time Sid has seen her dressed properly in years, and Sid feels a tinge of pride, though not enough to stop him from feeling annoyed. "I was just..." He reverts to his default position of carer. "Go and sit down, mum. I'm just gonna tidy up a bit."

Karen smiles helplessly. "There's no washing up liquid."

"There's a shop two minutes away."

Karen smiles again. "Go on, then."

Sid isn't in the mood. "Come on mum, you know the score. You know what the therapist said. One small trip out every day. I'll come with you if you want."

Karen shakes her head furiously. "I can't, son."

"Of course you can." Sid begins to scrub angrily at the dishes in the sink. "Life's not a *game*, mum."

Karen is shaken. "I know that, son. I'm trying, alright. I'm doing my best."

Sid's mobile phone begins to vibrate in his pocket. Sid ignores it.

"Aren't you going to answer it?" Karen hadn't meant to upset her son. She really is doing her best. It's just, it was all she could manage to get dressed today. She'd hoped that would be enough for Sid. He didn't have to *attack* her, no matter how bad a mood he was in.

Sid throws his unanswered phone on the kitchen counter. "I'm going out. I'll pick up some stuff on my way home."

"OK, son." Karen holds out her cheek, waiting for a kiss.

Sid reluctantly obliges.

After he has gone, Karen checks his phone to see who has got him so riled up. *12 missed calls - Scott.* She places the phone back where he left it and pads back through to her new nest on the sofa. Maybe there's a way she can make it up to him. Give his room a quick hoover, something like that.

Sid's head is still spinning when he gets home from the shop. He'd been walking past Nanda's, his mind stuck in a loop that went future-Scott-past-Scott-future, over and over for the past few days. It was easy to avoid Scott since his last day at school, given he was banned from the premises. Now that they had sold the last of the alcohol to the Watsons, they had severed all the commitments that brought them together. There was still the cleaning business. Sid guessed that Scott would be spending his days doing that, keener than ever to prove everyone wrong. There was no point in trying to find a new school. Right before exams? No one would have him.

Scott's swift exit had left a void in Sid's life that no one else could fill. Not Reashan, with his invitations to kick a ball about at lunchtime. Not Leila, with her music recommendations written on pages torn from her notebook and slipped to him during lessons. Not even his mum, with her efforts at cooking and the small comforts that made these days of recovery bearable for her. There was nobody like Scott.

Sid had noticed that the shutters were up. He'd slunk into the shop, his apology tumbling out wholeheartedly the second he saw Mr Nanda. He was unprepared for the forgiveness. When Mr Nanda had thanked him for everything he'd done to help Reashan and his family – when he'd looked Sid in the eye and said that he and Scott were good, good boys – Sid's heart had just about stopped.

By the time he arrives home, he has figured it out. Olsen would be gone in a month, a blip in the timetable of Sid's life. But the thought of a life without his best friend. He couldn't do it. This life, this way of being in the world. Figuring things out, changing things for the better. He couldn't do any of it without Scott.

CHAPTER 18

Life after school has been good to them. Scott wasn't joking when he told Olsen he had bigger fish to fry: his first day of freedom, he had drawn up a plan of action and he is intent on achieving his goals. Phase Two: Party Planning. There'd been a small hiccup, though. After simmering alone for over a week, Sid had finally promised to join Scott on one condition. They'd sat outside York Minster at midnight, the gargoyles adding a cinematic judgement to the scene made Scott smile despite the occasion.

Sid had confessed everything. Said he was terrified of ending up like his mum. Scott had promised not to let him, tried to convince him that normal was over-rated. They'd locked horns for a while, jutting back and forth over the same old fears. Sid's eternal dilemma of wanting to be liked. Needing approval from strangers. His fear of being "weird." And Scott's unflinching belief in himself and his friend. Sid wasn't about to give up on A-levels, and he was insistent that Scott should have options, too. He'd made a deal with Scott. A kind of ferocious glint in his eye that made Scott realise Sid would walk away forever if he didn't agree. As such, Scott found himself hiring a private tutor and studying at home. He gave his share of the cleaning business to Leila; Sid's went to

Reashan. They owed the Nandas that much. Free to live a life that didn't feel like a compromise for either of them, they burned the candle at both ends, their collective minds switching seamlessly between party planning and studying.

Scott stares hard at the problem, the culmination of two years of studying at home. Away from the pressure of school, inquisitive eyes and a maths teacher intent on embarrassing him, Scott finds that the numbers dance around a little less. He can finally focus. He's already finished his A-level exams, handed in his coursework, but there's something still niggling him, a part of the equation he doesn't quite get. He's never understood people who study just for the sake of passing an exam: surely, the whole point is to engage your brain, to learn and to retain the knowledge. He has commandeered one wall of his bedroom, entirely covered it in enormous white sheets of paper, scrawled with sums. It reminds him of the college scenes in 'A Beautiful Mind'. God, thinks Scott, scratching his head. Sometimes he feels like John Nash. But he'll finish it tonight, he has to. It's just a question of stripping it all back, starting at the beginning. Scott turns up his music and concentrates.

Sid takes a sip of his cool beer, stretches out on the grass and looks up. The clouds are fluorescent against the clear blue sky. A new summer up ahead and then, beyond... he reaches for his camera and snaps. The digital camera is his pride and joy and he keeps it in pristine condition. He tucks it under his knees to protect it from the sun. He loves the fact that he is building up a portfolio of his new life. It's not just his photography skills that are improving with time; Sid is beginning to learn that people like him just as he is.

Leila and Reashan are stretched out on the grass next to him, their conversation typically impenetrable, full of codes and in-jokes they aren't even aware of. Sid zones out.

It's been a long time coming, this feeling of... what is it, freedom? he's experiencing now. Opening up to Scott, admitting that his mum needed help, that had been the hard part. Everything since - the two years that led to him being here, on the grass, a beer in hand, past four o'clock, with two great friends and a headful of dreams - well, that had just kind of happened. Scott's seventeenth birthday, and they had driven over to Leeds for a night out. Surrounded by people he trusted, getting drunk hadn't seemed like such a big deal. Privately, he'd set himself some rules: only one beer per hour, no mixing and never in front of his mum. Publicly, though, Sid Sadowskyj was like any other teenager looking down the barrel of a long summer. So what if he hadn't quite got the grades to get into Oxford. There were more important things than that, like sticking close to his friends.

He tunes back into their conversation.

Reashan is interrogating his sister and she is not backing down.

"I just don't get it!" Reashan is waving his arms in his sister's face. "University's for pussies."

Leila rolls her eyes. "Can you please not use that word."

"I just don't get it!" he repeats. "We've got our cleaning business, we're making more money than we need, we're looking after our family. Why do you wanna do something so selfish as go to uni? You never commit to anything."

Leila is indignant. "Don't talk to me about commitment. I worked my arse off to get straight As. Who says I want to stay at home and work for the family? It has to change sometime. I wanna stand on my own two feet. Besides, this is pointless. I've already got my place at York." She pouts defiantly. "I don't care what you or mum or anyone says, I'm going."

Reashan and Leila simmer for a minute. Then, without warning or discussion, they ambush Sid. "What do you think?" they ask simultaneously, their faces wearing the same expression.

Sid is a little freaked out. The dialogue is the exact one that he imagines he'll have to have with Scott over the next few days. Sid's acceptance letter into York Uni had arrived this morning. He's due to start in six weeks. He has no idea how to broach the subject with Scott. He takes the chance to practice his speech. "I've always wanted to go to university. I think it's important. Meet new people, get a new perspective on things. It's not just about the learning. It's a whole new challenge."

Leila smiles at her brother, smugly. "See. We're not all cretins like you."

"I got into York, too." Sid beams at Leila. It feels good to say it out loud. He hasn't even told his mum yet. He reckons she'll be alright with it. He'll still be close to home and he can visit her every weekend, even pop over to cook for her a couple of nights a week. Besides, his mum always wanted him to go to uni. She'll be proud as punch, even if her initial reaction suggests otherwise.

"Sidney, mate, you're kidding?" Reashan sounds genuinely let down. "But you're the one that showed me there's more to life than school. Nah, mate, you're selling out to the man."

Sid laughs. "The man? The whole anti-school thing, that's more Scott, really. I actually quite liked school." The sky above darkens. "There is no... I'm not selling out."

Reashan holds up his hand in protest. "Whatever, mate."

"So, what you gonna study?" asks Leila.

"Events Management."

Now it is Reashan's turn to laugh. "But that's what you do already. You mean, you're gonna pay for the privilege of three years doing what you could be paid to do as a job. Everyone in town already knows you guys! You and Scott throw the best events!"

Sid is defensive. "It's more for the theory. The business side of things."

Reashan cracks open another beer. "Business schmizness," he says.

Leila glares at her brother. "You should do what makes you happy," she tells Sid.

Seeing Sid's face, Reashan backs off a little. "Yeah. I mean, whatever. It's nothing to do with me." He holds up his bottle to his friends. "See you on the other side!"

After the conversation has moved on, Sid sits more quietly than before. Reashan had said everything that Scott would. It hadn't exactly gone to plan. Sid would have to re-think his strategy. Maybe there was a way to convince Scott that university could work for him, too. If he's honest, Sid isn't exactly ready to go it alone just yet. It'd be great if Scott could be there alongside him. Think of the adventures they'd have, the new friends they'd make.

Scott's head is still buzzing when he joins his friends in the park. The expanse of green is covered with people like them, making the most of a warm night. The smoke of a dozen barbecues drifts temptingly towards him. He sprawls on the grass, glad to finally be out of the house. "Have you guys eaten?" he asks.

Leila throws a packet of crisps towards him, and Scott grabs a handful.

"So what's new?" he asks. Though he has absolutely no desire to enter the sixth form building, Scott enjoys hearing his friends' tales about college. It seems that everything over there is exactly like school, only a little more extreme. The tutors range from art-school hippies who drink herbal tea in the darkroom at lunchtime to an obsessive chemistry teacher who thinks that mobile phones are the spawn of the devil. Scott is glad to be free of all that. He turns to Sid. "Did you tell them?

"Tell them what?" asks Sid, a little anxious. He can't possibly know, can he?

"About that pitch we did at Blackpool Ballroom."

Sid looks animated. "It looks like the Eiffel Tower. Is that what you mean?"

Scott frowns at his friend. The smallest things impress Sid sometimes. "I meant what *happened*."

Leila and Reashan wait expectantly. They love Scott when he's in this kind of a mood. They can practically see the ideas reverberating in his mind like a pinball machine. He's an inspiring guy to be around.

Scott plays up to his audience. "The room was a massive brick cavern and they were sitting behind a table at the far end of it. That walk across the hallway felt like forever. It gave the panel enough time to size us up. I'd barely introduced us to the six of them when they turned to each other and sniggered."

Sid shakes his head at the memory. "Mate, it wasn't sniggering. They were screeching with laughter. We hadn't prepared for that."

"It was rude," says Scott. "I don't care how old someone is, it was disrespectful. We weren't there on work experience, trick-or-treating, singing Christmas carols. We were there as equals. They must have seen it in our faces. Eventually, they gave us the time we deserved. Go," he points to Sid.

"An event is not just a night out, an evening away from the kids..." begins Sid.

"Nor is it just an excuse to have a couple of drinks..." continues Scott. "It's an experience. Something that will change the way you think..." Scott smiles and glances at Leila to gauge her interest.

"At this point, the lights dim, we can hear some faint music starting up in the background and they're beginning to look a little worried. I carry on with the speech. Tingle every sense and create..."

"A night to remember," finishes Sid.

Leila smiles at the boys. Sometimes, Scott and Sid are even more of a double act than she and Reashan. There is art to the way they work around each other's strengths, and never make a big deal out of their individual weaknesses.

Scott smiles back. "I didn't think we could pull it off. We'd called in every favour. It was like an A-Z of everyone we'd ever come into contact with, like that final scene in 'The Game'. Have you seen that, where Michael Douglas stumbles into the canteen? It was surreal. Exactly as I'd planned. First, the unicyclists, one from each doorway, whizzing across the centre of the room. There was a man breathing fire. They'd all dressed the part. It was like a cabaret act. There was no doubt that these guys were professionals and that, by default, made us pros too. I missed the break dancers. I was too busy watching the faces of the council members. It took them a while to realise what was happening, but we did it. We transported them from what they'd assumed would be a boring sales pitch. By the end, they were all dancing."

"We got the gig," says Sid.

"I don't know what they told people when they got back to the council headquarters, but we obviously left a good impression. Our phones didn't stop ringing the rest of the week." Scott takes a self-satisfied swig from his beer. "The kind of money old Olsen could never even dream of."

"So, we're going out tonight, then?" asks Reashan.

"I can't," says Sid. "Social worker's coming round."

His friends nod in acceptance. Though Leila and Reashan had always had their suspicions about Sid's home life, it wasn't until Sid

215

confessed last year that they realised just how bad it had been. When it comes to his mum, Sid gets the night off, no questions asked.

CHAPTER 19

Scott slowly gathers up the cards from the table and shuffles them. He's been playing Solitaire for the best part of an hour. This is always his favourite time of the night, after all the tasks have been ticked off, when Sid is relaxed enough to represent them both and Scott is free to find a quiet place in the club to hunker down and take stock. His soft black leather notebook sits beside the half-finished game, and he writes in it when the thoughts come. The money is counted and already in the safe.

Scott glances down onto the dance floor. Leila is there with a male friend from college, talking intensely in the corner and Scott can't help but feel a little jealous. The whole summer had felt like a slow dance with her. They found themselves bumping into each other on the streets around town, their paths accidentally and irrevocably in sync. Scott can't even begin to contemplate having a girlfriend. It's never been about the girls for him. His and Sid's mission seems bigger than that. Scott can't afford to be sidetracked.

"Good night?" he asks, as Sid bounds up the staircase. It takes Sid a while to find his feet at an event. Scott always has to be around for the first couple of hours, just to boost Sid's confidence a little. But all it takes is one compliment, one look from a girl, and Sid is fine on his own.

"Something like that," says Sid.

Scott glances down. Lucy Rogan, Sid's out-of-reach all-time-favourite-girl-since-primary-school is blowing a kiss towards Sid.

Sid can't hide his happiness. "She asked if we want to come to hers after. Her parents are away. I've been chatting her up all night but I think she's more into you, to be honest." Sid looks at the mess on the table around Scott. "God knows why," he mutters under his breath. "Anyway, she made me come up here and ask you if you want to come."

"I'm good, thanks," says Scott, his mind already moving onto other things. He's had an idea about the next event. The past month has been Party, Sleep, Plan, Repeat and he is growing tired of the routine. He's lost count of the number of girls he's watched Sid pull on the dance floor, the number of times he's walked in on things he wished he hadn't. Events are fine, and they've made good money off the back of it, but Scott is bored. He has an idea in mind for something bigger. "Go to Lucy's." He looks up. "Mate, that's a big deal. I know how much you like her. You should go for it." He smiles. "I can tie things up here."

"Nah, I'll stay til the end," offers Sid. He feels like he should. Scott never looks like he is having a good time. The least Sid can do is help to clear up at the end of the night.

"Just go, have fun. I'll call you tomorrow," says Scott, already distracted and lost in his notes, waving a dismissive goodbye to Sid. A minute later, stuck on a word that he can't bring to mind, he glances down at the dance floor. He watches as Sid lifts aside Lucy's hair to whisper something in her ear, takes her hand and leads her out of the club. Scott stands up, reaches across to the nearby table and takes a swig of beer from the bottle he's been cradling all night.

Scott's new plan is a giant step up. His strategy is simple: aim bigger, earn bigger. They are ready for it.

Pitching to entire Boards is daunting, having to stand up there in front of the suits and state his case. There'd always been that dichotomy in Scott's personality: he isn't afraid to stand out in every aspect of his daily philosophy, but he works hard on his public persona when it comes to business. Nerves are something else, though. They creep up on him, silently and before he knows it, it's too late, and he's running for the bathroom, splashing water on his face, trying to remember how to breathe. No matter how thoroughly he knows the clients or how confident he is in the pitch, he is always overwhelmed by dread.

Scott's tuxedo jacket catches on the rough brick as he pushes through the double doors. He checks the damage. First time he's worn this suit. He can't afford to make a mistake today. Council Boards are notoriously difficult to impress. They are always looking to save public money, cut corners. That's why Scott had insisted on no expense spared with this one. It doesn't matter how uncomfortable he feels. The tux is part of the deal. He rubs at his elbow.

It is a warren of a building. Factories like this are abundant around Yorkshire, relics of an industrial heritage long gone to the dogs. It's all well and good, thinks Scott, converting the disused buildings into conference halls and venues, and he understands that these things take time, but running around a labyrinthine factory looking for the toilet isn't his idea of a pre-pitch routine. His phone rings. "Where are you?" Scott shouts, his voice reverberating around the empty building. "It's nearly time."

Sid's voice is fraught with simmering panic. "I'm not coming. We need to talk."

Sid's been avoiding the issue for as long as he can and he's beginning to worry that Scott will hear it from someone else. He chooses the flashiest place he can think of to meet. The kind of restaurant full of old people who hate a scene, where the marble columns and old-school glamour make you want to speak in hushed tones. A backdrop of reverie. Wishful thinking.

Scott screams at him across the table. "It's just stupid!"

"It's not stupid." Sid waits for the cutlery to stop rattling, steadies the table. "It'll be fun."

"I mean, what do you even wanna study?" Scott's voice is accusatory, his arms folded across his chest, waiting to be impressed. God, he'd love Sid to throw him something he couldn't shoot down. It'd make a nice change, not having to battle him at every turn. He'd love to be able to just holds his hands up, acknowledge defeat for once. Life would be so much easier.

"I don't mind," says Sid. "It's more about the experience."

Fuck's sake, thinks Scott. Predictable. He looks around him, notes the tiny touch across the table of the couple next to them, watches the pianist's hands move across the minor key as she plays her heart out, hears the rain tapping a staccato beat on the glass dome above their heads. It's *all* experience, every second of life. You just have to tune your mind into the details. He gives Sid the benefit of the doubt. "What, like film?" he suggests. "I mean, I think I could handle that. It'll help with our movie."

"I knew you'd say that. I checked. Film course is fully booked." Sid moves his hand to the bridge of his nose, an absent-minded habit from years spent wearing glasses. "I was thinking... Events Management? It could be fun."

Scott scoffs. "You serious?" His boot kicks at the table again as he leans forward. These tables were made for polite conversation. "What the hell have we been *doing*? We've got the best client list in the north."

"I know that," says Sid. "But we can do it the right way this time."

"What's the *right* way? Mr 'hi-I'm-a-pretend-academic-called-Dave-who-just-wants-to-sleep-with-all-the-hot-students' is gonna show us how it's done?"

"What? Look, just treat it like a holiday."

"Jesus!" The table shakes again. "You wanna go on holiday, let's go! We can go anywhere in the world."

Sid tries to get the waiter's attention, ask for some water, but the man keeps taking the long route around their table, giving them a wide berth. He gives up. "I don't want to. I want to go to university and get a degree."

"But they have ponytails."

"Eh? What? Look, you haven't been so you don't know, Scott."

Scott takes a long sip of his own water. "Nah. It's not for me. Can't do it."

It takes Sid a while to answer. In the background, the pianist is playing something slow and innocuous, supposed to be soothing. "Then I'll go on my own," he says, quietly.

Scott stares at his best mate. "University. It's back to *school*. What are they gonna teach you, anyway?" He can't believe he's having to spell it out. "You pay someone to tell you what's on the internet for free. And what are we doing right now?" He gestures at his notebook on the table between them, stuffed full of contacts, events, ideas. "I mean, seriously. If you want to be a doctor, a lawyer, go to uni, I get it but…"

"I want to meet people."

Scott throws up his arms in despair, gesticulates wildly to the tables around them. "You're surrounded by people!"

"Sshhhh," hisses Sid.

"OK." Scott knows how Sid works. A bit of give and take. Maybe he's being too harsh. "I'll go for a month or two. Yeah? That'll be cool. We'll take a month off."

"No." Sid is adamant. No half measures. "I wanna *go.*"

"Fine. Six months, but that's ages."

"The full thing. Three years."

Scott has been tracing his butter knife against the silk of the tablecloth. He lets it fall. "Three years?" he hisses. "Fuck, Sid, that's a long time. Look, why don't we just work our arses off now. Learn business, learn life, meet people. For the rest of our lives, not just at uni." He doesn't care that people are staring. He's never given a shit about that. "I mean, life should be a canvas full of dots and different sizes and colours..." He looks at Sid, pleading.

Sid sighs. It's kinda sad. Scott's giving it his best shot but there's nothing he could say that'll make Sid make change his mind on this one. He's never felt so certain about anything. He finds his voice again. "So, I'm putting it on the list. Yeah?"

"I'll give you my share of the events money," suggests Scott. It's a long shot but hey. He knows how far that money could go for Sid, what it would mean for him and his mum. She could put down a deposit on a new house, make a fresh start.

It's Sid's turn to shout. "No, Scott, you're missing the point entirely! Please just give it a try for me. It'll be fun. It'll be a blast, honestly." He gets up to leave, needing a break from this. He can barely think in this place, Scott raging across the table at him, all these strangers looking at them.

"Where you going?" Scott snaps.

"To the toilet."

"Hang on, hold on." Scott struggles to think of an ace card.

Sid reads his mind. There is no ace card. Not this time. "It's going on the list, Scott."

"Fuck's sake!" shouts Scott. The table and its contents clatter to the floor as he fails to hold it in any longer. The waiter comes running. Scott ignores him. He stares at Sid to check this is actually happening. "Really?"

CHAPTER 20

Hepworth House has none of the stately home grandeur that the name conjures. The sixties tower block is one of seven identical buildings that have been purpose-built to house eight hundred freshers a safe distance from residential areas. The architects have gone to all the usual efforts in creating a university campus: a corner shop that stocks shelves of baked beans and sixteen pence noodles; a big red post-box for sending letters home; an artificial pond with a couple of ducks and a canteen in the centre that serves fish fingers and dubious-looking vegetables. Monday is parcel day. In the weeks to come, Sid will traipse down to the office and check the pigeon hole marked 'S' to see if his mum has remembered to write the postcard she promised.

Scott still can't believe that, with all the money he's stashed away over the summer, Sid has chosen to live here. Even if he hadn't wanted to live with Scott, he could have had his pick of places, rented a big town house right near the park. Scott will never understand why he's chosen to isolate himself way out here, with all the other losers.

"Dude, are you coming in or what?"

Scott looks up. The student must be about twenty. He is wearing skinny jeans and a too-tight retro T-shirt, designed to fit a ten-year-old.

He's been blowing liquorice tobacco smoke in Scott's face for the past ten minutes. Now, he is holding the door open for him. Scott can't believe he agreed to give this uni thing a go.

"Nah," says Scott. "I wouldn't go in there if you paid me."

The student's smile disappears. "Whatever, yuppie" he spits. He glares at Scott as he rounds the stairs and gets swallowed by the building.

"Sidney!" greets Scott as his friend finally appears. "Looking good! Is that a new hoodie?"

"Very funny," sneers Sid. "What you doing wearing a waistcoat? We're going to a lecture, not a sales pitch."

Scott laughs and puts his arm around Sid's shoulder. He'd had a re-think of his wardrobe recently. If he was going to play the part of uni student, spend most of his days in the company of carbon-copy droids, he might as well make an effort to stand out. His waistcoat is designer and it makes him feel smart, although his head is far from composed.

"Seriously, mate," says Sid. "You're dressed like my old sociology teacher. Have you not unpacked yet or something?"

They take the shortcut. Someone has made an effort to construct neat paths around the skirting of the buildings, but no one ever uses them. Instead, Sid and Scott traipse across the grass like everyone else. Sid joins the end of a long queue.

"What you doing?" asks Scott.

"It's only ten minutes on the bus. They come every ten minutes." Sid pulls a bottle of orange juice from his rucksack and begins to drink.

Scott eyes the line suspiciously. "This is stupid. I'll get us a taxi."

"Can't we just wait with everyone else?"

"To be honest..." Scott takes a swig from Sid's bottle. "I don't really fancy getting on a stinking bus with this lot."

Sid rolls his eyes. The girl in front turns around and gives Scott a glare.

Scott shakes off her rage. He's not gonna censor himself. An opinion is an opinion. He's not about to tone himself down just so that Sid can have an easy life. He pulls out his phone. "What's the address?" he asks Sid, covering the mouthpiece as the taxi receptionist answers.

It only takes five minutes across the park to reach the School of Leisure and Tourism but, paying the taxi driver and looking around, Scott has a feeling that the students from the bus queue have somehow been fast-tracked ahead of him and Sid. There seems to be the exact same menagerie of hoodies, rucksacks and too-loud voices in this part of town. Scott is glad he's worn his suit. He pauses at a bench to put his wallet back into his leather satchel. It's like being back at school. Nobody knows where the hell they fit in. His head is spinning.

"You're not going to start wearing the same clothes every day and stop washing, are you?" he asks.

Sid laughs. "As if that's about to happen."

"Don't turn into one of those uni bums." Scott checks around him. He is serious. All the money people spent of fees and the place still looked like a throwback to the seventies. "I'm pretty pissy, Sid. Feels like a waste of..."

Sid turns and looks Scott in the eyes. "Scott. Have fun. Enjoy it." Sid takes a deep breath. Anyone else and he'd have marched on ahead, but it's Scott. They come as a pair. He feels a responsibility to prove his point, to make Scott enjoy it. He waits for Scott to catch up. The timetable says 'Room B12'. Sid glances up at the building ahead. It is a series of hexagons, built on top of each other at strange angles, like a slab of dissolving honeycomb. They are about to get lost, he can tell. There are dozens of other people, chatting in groups or clutching their folders to their chests and trying to look unafraid. Sid swallows back the feeling of nervousness that lurks as a residue of his past shyness, and strides through them all, reassuring himself that he'll know at least some of their names by the end of the day. Once inside the building, he drops his rucksack on a tattered seat and turns to Scott. Sid frowns. Scott has disappeared.

Sid stands up on the chair and surveys the crowd. "For fuck's sake," he mutters. Scott is crouching down by the side of some trees, away from the main crowd. Sid navigates his way back out of the building.

"What you doing?" he asks, trying not to sound angry. Scott's games have been increasingly more testing lately. Ever since Scott had reluctantly agreed to give uni a go, he'd had fits of weirdness on a daily basis. Sid is losing his patience. He refuses to be late for his first class.

Scott looks up. His forehead is flecked with beads of sweat. He is struggling to breathe.

"What's going on?" asks Sid. He places his hand on Scott's back. His waistcoat is damp. "Take this thing off."

"You think..." Scott stammers as he sits back on his heels. "I'm sorry, I don't want to ruin this for you. I'm not doing it on purpose."

Sid helps Scott to his feet. "It's only the beginning. Calm down, take a day at a time. Stop worrying! OK?" He smiles and picks up Scott's satchel from the ground. "I promise, it's gonna be fun."

Scott still feels weak but he forces himself through the crowd, following Sid up and down flights of stairs as they search for the classroom. He feels like a cumbersome whale swimming in Sid's slipstream as he bumps his way behind him. I'm good, I'm good, he tells himself. By the time they locate B12 in the basement, Scott is

227

thinking more positively. "So, what do you wanna do for lunch?" he asks, reminding himself that the class only lasts a couple of hours. They'd had events meetings that lasted for five.

Sid laughs as he pushes open the door.

The bright yellow paint of the room does nothing to detract from the fact that there are no windows.

"It's not how I thought it would be," says Sid, scanning the room. He'd imagined a grand room with high ceilings, possibly a marble statue or two overlooking proceedings. A proper seat of learning. It is full of students, some perched on tables, others chatting away as though they've known each other for years. He spots two seats third row from the front.

"It's *exactly* how I thought it would be," mutters Scott, following Sid and taking the seat beside him.

"Hey mate, wassup?"

The lad looks friendly enough, but Scott really can't be arsed. "Yeah," he answers, avoiding eye contact. This is all too familiar. School days were supposed to be behind him. He doesn't notice the lecturer walking in. When Scott does look up, he is appalled to see the face that matches the voice.

The lecturer is struggling to make his voice heard above the clamour. "Guys…guys…guys guys…guys guys guys… and girls. Hi. How are you and welcome to my class "Event Management" at…"

Scott zones out. He glances at Sid. Sid is already taking notes. Scott looks again at the lecturer. How is he expected to take this guy seriously? The man is about fifty but he hasn't told his clothes this. His jeans are ripped at the thigh. He is wearing a faded ACDC vest top with an Oxfam jacket. He hasn't even shaved his stubble, for Christ's sake. It is evident, from the way he sits on the edge of the table with his legs wide open, and talks as though he is addressing an opera house, that he loves himself. Scott drops his head into his hands. The floor is also yellow, patterned with tiny swirls that are beginning to move, so that Scott has the creeping sensation that he always has when he's ill, that he is staring into a rock pool full of worms, wriggling over each other, trying to work their way under his skin. "I don't feel too good, Sid," he mumbles.

Sid dismisses him and looks back at the lecturer.

Scott can feel the sweat dripping down his temples and he presses his thumbs against his head to try to contain the pressure. This isn't the first time. Last time it happened, Reashan had been there, had told him to breathe, to focus on a point in the distance and... The lecturer is wearing a silver hoop in one ear. Scott stares at it and tries to pay attention.

"Don't worry," says the lecturer. "The first year is EeeeZeee." He contorts his fingers like a rapper.

This guy's a laugh, thinks Sid.

"We have a good time, get to know each other and party lots."

The class roars. Sid joins in the cheering and bangs on the table. It is a universe away from school.

Scott needs air. He locates the door and, stumbling up, begins to walk towards it, one step at a time, only his feet don't seem to be cooperating, and how is he expected to walk when the floor keeps wriggling?

"Scott...." Sid looks around. Everyone is watching Scott. The lecturer is sitting with a look of mild amusement on his face. Sid watches as Scott reaches for the door handle and misses. "Scott!" he yells, his chair clattering to the floor as he runs to help him.

"Alright, son?" The nurse smiles as she checks his blood pressure. It is early in the term for admissions like these. They usually come near exam time, when students are pulling all-night revision sessions and worrying about their word count.

Scott opens his eyes slowly. He is lying on a hospital bed. He raises his hand to his face. There is a mask over his mouth. He traces the thin tube to an oxygen canister suspended above his head.

"Lucky you were right next door to the hospital," says the nurse, with the easy kindness that comes from years of professional compassion.

"You knob head," says Sid, thrusting a carton of Ribena towards Scott. "You collapsed. Doctor says you had a panic attack."

Scott pulls off his mask. "I feel sick."

The nurse checks his temperature and writes the results on a clipboard. "That'll pass," she says. "Just lie down." She smiles at the boys. "I'll be back in a bit."

Scott lies back on the bed and sighs. "I'm sorry, Sid."

"Don't be stupid. Just relax."

"How long have I been here?"

"About five minutes," answers Sid.

"Five minutes?

"Yeah."

Scott takes a sip of Sid's drink. He has a sudden thought. "Anyone see me naked?"

Sid laughs. "No, why would they?" Hospitals make him nervous. He's just glad it's nothing serious. The lecturer had been decent about it. Told Sid that he should come straight back to class whenever he was done. That he should try not to miss the introductions. Getting to know his classmates was part of the fun, he'd said.

Scott looks out of the window behind Sid. He can see the hexagonal building from here. The crowd has disappeared. "I think my university days are over."

Sid shifts in his seat, crestfallen. "What? You're kidding, right?"

"I'm sorry Sid." Scott is out of the bed, lacing up his boots, looking for the door.

"Scott. Relax. Chill out. What you doing?"

"I can't." Scott can't believe he has to say them out loud. Sid should know better. He forced him into it. Scott had warned him that it wasn't in his blood to sit in a classroom, to do the right thing. And now his body had pathologically rejected the whole goddamn idea. He couldn't believe Sid still didn't get it.

"Scott I'm supposed to be in my first day of uni now. But I'm sat here with you. With you again. Why, Scott?" Sid can't believe this. For a second, he wonders if it had all been an act, a perfectly orchestrated excuse not to have to stay. Like the trick Sid had pulled in the maths classroom a couple of years earlier. Scott's capable of it, he knows he is.

"It's gonna take too long!" Scott screams. "It's three years! For what, a piece of paper?"

Sid feels cruel before the words have even come out of his mouth, but he has to say it. "I know that you wanna be *great*. But you don't always get what you want. We had fun. We did well. But it's time to stop being out of sync with everybody else." Sid shrugs. "I wanna be normal."

The sounds of the hospital – the beeps, the banging of doors, the students outside - have disappeared into irrelevance. It is just him and Sid in the room now, Scott seeing that same look in his friend's eyes that he's seen all summer, the lost-puppy look that asks, what the hell happens now? Scott wants to shake him and tell him that that's the beauty of it all. That they can do whatever they want to do. Scott scratches at the side of his temple. He's damned if he's ending up fucking *normal*. The time to act is now. "I am great, Sid, and so are you. We're gonna have a spectacular life, but this." He stops, clenches his fists tighter. "Is not what we're about." He looks around the room, despising everything, the sterility of it all. "I don't want normal. I want to wake up in the morning and do

231

something I love. I want to go to bed at night, look in the mirror and go, that was a great day. And there's a great day ahead and there's a great *future* ahead."

"That's what I'm doing now." Sid has listened patiently, like he always does, but he's just about ready to pack it in this time. Call it quits, leave Scott, his skewed manifesto that makes Sid feel like he's his fucking little rat. Scurrying down the tunnel in pursuit of whatever moral crusade Scott's flying the flag for this month.

"No, you're not, you're just trying to fit in and go with the flow." He tries to spell it out for Sid. "Look, you might be happy in a month or two, you might be happy in a year or two. But you're basing your fate... for the next *ten years*... on your weaknesses and your misdirection today."

Sid doesn't know what to say. It's like the past few months are being erased. Like that conversation outside York Minster, Sid spilling his guts, practically pleading with Scott to find a way to stay close, had never happened. He tries to be kind, maintain his composure. "Come on, Scott, I know that you wanna...."

Scott is adamant, unsinkable. He is furious. He's tried everything to get his point across. Sid just doesn't get it. Scott's aversion to academia is in his *soul*. Sometimes he wonders if Sid knows him at all. He screams. "It's not for me!"

Sid sits still. He's never heard Scott shout like that before. "It's what I want..." says Sid, quietly.

"Look, if you wanna go..." It takes effort for Scott to say the next words. Everything about it feels wrong. Like they're making a terrible mistake from which they might never recover. "If you wanna go, then go."

Sid sighs.

"Be the best you can be," Scott rants. "But if it's because you're too chicken-shit and you're choosing something just so you have somewhere to go for the next three years, then you're gonna look back on your life with regret. You'll end up…"

"It's what I want," says Sid. He knows what Scott was about to say. *You'll end up like your mum.* But he's never been so sure of anything. He's proud of himself, despite how crap it feels. Proud to have swum against the tide for once. Wasn't that what everyone was always telling him to do?

Scott reaches for his jacket. "OK." He studies his friend's face, sees that Sid's mind is made up. He faces Sid, wonders when he'll see him next. If he shook Sid's hand right now, he'd crush it to powder. It's best just to leave. "Cool. Go for it."

CHAPTER 21

Winter comes and Sid finds himself spending as little time as possible in his halls of residence. True, his window on the eighth floor has an uninterrupted view over the city. He's positioned his new camera on a tripod in the window and he's captured a couple of brilliant slow-release night shots that he plans to give out as Christmas presents. He'd taken one for his mum, a blazing red sunrise that he thought summed up her potential for revival. But, the single glaze windows make him vulnerable to every biting wind that roars down from the moors or in from the sea. There are plenty of warmer places to be.

The neatly arranged fliers on his wall are organised by date of event. Looking at the grid, Sid considers his options. There is a traffic light party in the student union. Sid vetoes that; he's not quite ready to wear a green badge and take his chances with the other freshers. He wants something low-key tonight. Though he's too proud to admit it, he misses Scott. Sid wraps a cashmere scarf around his neck and pulls it tight. He checks himself in the tiny mirror above his sink and carefully dabs on some Clive Christian. Sid had discovered his scent while he was out looking for a birthday present for his mum. The cologne makes him feel polished and clean, adds an extra dimension to the image he is after. He smooths his palm across his beard. He still can't get used to the sight of it - it makes him feel disorganised, as though he's forgotten to put pants on in the morning - but women seem to like it. It is fine to try things like that out here. His new life has taken him away from his usual haunts and he rarely runs into anyone from school anymore.

Sid wonders whether, if he sits still long enough, people will forget he is there. The student house is cloaked in smoke, a heady mix of incense and weed. Sid has a headache. The solitary beer he's been nursing since he arrived is down to the dregs, but he doesn't want to risk moving. There is a wall of strangers between him and the fridge. Sid checks his phone again. Still nothing. He wonders if Scott has lost his number. Worse, deleted it. He's scared to be the first to call.

He locates the bathroom and locks the door behind him. He leans against the sink and has a word with himself. *The whole point,* he says aloud, *of coming to uni.* He splashes cold water onto his face. *Is to meet new people. You are in a house full of new people. These people are potential friends.* His reflection stares back at him, unconvinced. *Now get out there and make an effort.*

The sun is rising when he leaves the party, still stone-cold sober and gripped by an urgent desire to call his mum. He decides against it. He passes no-one on the walk across campus, but he is always surprised by how many lights are on at dawn.

He taps his room key against his trousers and glances at the silhouette of the tower blocks against the navy-and-rust sky. A good morning for photographs. He begins to compose the perfect image in his head. Last Sunday, he'd picked up a new lens at the specialist shop in town. There are a couple of new techniques he wants to try.

Scott lets himself into Hepworth House. It's easy. The security guard on the front desk is immersed in the Argos catalogue, a calculator on the desk beside him. There are a dozen fluorescent post-it notes stuck to the toy section. Christmas is coming. Scott checks the guard's name badge as he passes. "Good night, Mr Travers?" he asks politely.

"Aye, not bad, lad, not bad," the security guard answers, giving Scott an uncertain smile.

Scott takes the stairs two at a time. Living in town has its perks. The cinema is across the road from his flat and, when he isn't in the mood for the company of strangers, the widescreen TV is the next best thing. Some nights, he just starts walking. Tonight, he'd been on a midnight stroll and his feet carried him to Sid's halls without any real sense of purpose.

Since they'd gone their separate ways in September, Scott had had the distinct feeling that Sid was ignoring him. The minutes between texts had stretched into days then weeks and lately, nothing. It is a phase, it has to be. Sid's just trying out his wings. Christmas holidays are around the corner, and Sid is too sociable not to call his best friend to tell him his gossip. Scott knows he should probably just hold tight and wait for the call. But he is here now. It would be rude not to say hi.

Definitely modelled on a prison he thinks again as he reaches Sid's floor. The main corridor is a perfect square that looks down onto an inner "garden" that is nothing more than a slab of concrete.

On each floor, the design is the same: bedrooms line two sides of the block, bathrooms another and the kitchen is a makeshift room with camping stove, toaster and microwave on the fourth side of the square. Each corridor is lined with windows, so that it is impossible to walk from bathroom to bedroom without being seen. Scott shudders. There is nowhere to hide. Everyone can see everything. He suddenly feels thankful for the extra money he's put into his new place: the seclusion of his bedroom, with its view over the park. Having the penthouse means that he can sit out on the balcony and know that nobody is watching. He is fine with not knowing his neighbours. They never cross paths on the stairs and their parties don't bother him. The close proximity of a dozen decent takeaways means he never has to cook.

He knocks firmly. The book in his satchel is a heavy hardback, an inspirational autobiography that's taking Scott forever to read, and it suddenly crosses his mind that maybe this is the catalyst Sid needs. Scott tucks the book under his arm and knocks again. He roots around in his bag for a pen and scribbles a message on the title page. He tries a third time.

CHAPTER 22

There were only so many times Scott could tackle Grand Theft Auto as a single player. By the nineteenth of December, he swallows his pride and dials. He is desperate to see his friend. The past few months working at the school have hardened him, reduced his days to solitary routine. He hates to say it, but he's become a nine til five man. For all his promises of coming over to hang out, Reashan has yet to visit once. Scott needs to laugh. He's fed up of waiting.

Sid has been looking at the same page on the textbook for half an hour. The coffee he'd picked up on the way home from five-a-side is cold, but he takes a slurp anyway, just for something to do. He frowns at the page. Wednesdays from three til five is one of his designated times for revision. Usually he just gets his head down, puts on his headphones and focuses. This afternoon, though, he can't settle. He'd thought the football might improve his mood but if anything, he now feels lower than before. So much for endorphins, he thinks. When the screen lights up on his phone, Sid doesn't even check the name. He answers without thinking.

"Sidney!" comes the voice on the end of the line. Scott is surprised that he's answered.

Sid swings his legs over the edge of the bed. "How are you, dude? I've missed you."

"Me too," says Scott. "Can we meet?"

Sid grins, snapping his text book closed. "Yeah, when?"

"Now."

"Yeah, cool, are you not in work?"

"I'm meant to be at the staff Christmas meal but, er...Olsen's put me next to Mr Fell."

"Hang on, back up. Olsen?"

"I'll explain later."

"Where are you?"

"Have a look out your window."

From the lilt in Scott's voice, Sid can tell he is smiling. He lifts the sash window and looks down. Scott is standing on the grass, a fire in his eyes as though he's just been in battle and won.

"That's creepy," laughs Sid. He grabs his keys from the table and throws them down.

"Don't you get claustrophobic?" asks Scott, leaning back on Sid's chair and looking around at what he considers his friend's temporary cage. He takes a sip of the Earl Grey tea that Sid has prepared for him, his fingers tracing the raised font on The Godfather mug. He wonders if Sid has got round to watching yet, whether the mug's just for show. It seems to Scott that there are certain emblems that university students need to possess in order to feel legit. Sid's room is no exception. Scott ticks them off as he looks around. A 'Trainspotting' poster. A hoodie with the uni's name broadcast all over it. Fucking fairy lights.

"It's been two months," says Sid. "Can you believe that? What have you been up to?"

"I got a job. How's uni?" Scott pretends not to be bothered by the fact that, amongst all the faces and all the good times depicted on the photos on Sid's wall, Scott can't see a trace of their own friendship. It's as though it never existed.

"It's good. Where are you working?" Sid thinks if he says it out loud he might manage to convince himself. "I'm having fun. The work seems a little..."

"At our old school. I'm chief copy monkey. Reprographics Overseer, is my full title." Scott stares at his friend. "Are you ready for what's next?"

"Hang on, you got a job at our old school? Working for Olsen? But you hate that place. Wait... for what's next? What do you mean what's next?" asks Sid.

"To become Sid," says Scott. "To breathe your own breath and speak your own words. To be remembered and spoken about for years to come!"

Sid clicks his fingers. "That!" he says. "Right there! Ah, I've missed you, man." He laughs.

"I'm serious," says Scott.

Sid studies Scott's face. He looks older than before. He's finally shed his puppy fat. He's dressed like in the old days, ripped cargo pants and scuffed-up boots, sunglasses on the top of his head, but his focus seems laser-beam straight and pointed right at him. It dawns on Sid that Scott really isn't joking. Sid hasn't got the energy for another row. "You're living in a movie, mate."

Scott stares back at him. "And it'll be our movie." Scott smiles as he notices the Dreamchasers list tacked up on the wall behind Sid's bed, almost out of sight. "Ultimate aim. Or had you forgotten?" he asks, accusingly.

Sid's mp3 player is still blasting through the headphones. In the silence, the tinny lyrics annoy them both. Sid switches it off. "Where you living?" he asks Scott.

"Moved out of my mum's. Too clean." He smiles, wonders if Sid has the same image he does, the two of them in the early days: days spent knocking on doors, the start of it all. He reaches into his jacket, rips a page from his notebook and borrows Sid's fountain pen to write his address. "It's by the park," he says, handing it to Sid, ink smeared all over his hands.

Sid nods. "Nice for you." He blows on the piece of paper to dry it, pins the address carefully to his noticeboard.

The two of them sit in silence, for too long to be comfortable. Scott speaks first. "Seriously, mate, that's all you've got? Small talk?" Sid doesn't know where to begin.

"After everything we've been through? What, we have to start all over again? Really?" He holds out his hand. "Scott Elliott."

Sid swipes his hand away.

"Come on!" says Scott, looking around at Sid's possessions. "Stop wasting your time. Wake up, man."

"Jesus, Scott. I haven't seen you in ages and you come in and..."

"This is the last time I'll ask," continues Scott. "But come on, let's go on an adventure together. Let's change the world." He stands up quickly and pulls the Dreamchasers list from the wall. "Let's do it."

Sid holds his head in his hands. "I think you should go," he says quietly, then seems to change his mind almost instantly, standing up, wrenching open the door.

Scott follows him out of his bedroom, along the corridor and into the kitchen. "You're the greatest person I know, Sid!" he shouts after him. "But you don't see it."

"Don't," says Sid, gritting his teeth. He closes the kitchen door behind them. This whole week. He'd been so excited about going home for Christmas, finally getting to cut free from this place for a couple of weeks, getting to spend some time with his mum and making peace with Scott and now here he is, fucking everything up, before he's even packed. He can see it all ahead of him now. Two weeks stuck in the house, trying to pretend everything is normal, bored out of his mind with no one to call. Leila and Reashan will take Scott's side. It'd be like being fourteen again. He will be completely alone. He yanks open the fridge and steals a can of beer from someone else's shelf. He wipes his eyes and scrapes a chair across the floor as he takes a long swig. He feels almost instantly better. "I'm really not," he says, scoffing at Scott's words. He hasn't had the guts to tell his story to anyone he's met here. They're all too caught up in their own minor dramas. But he can feel it, the shame, dragging behind him, stopping him from being completely upfront, making him fabricate lies about his family, the places he's been. And it makes him feel like shit: like he's betraying his mum and erasing his history. Scott was a one off. It was a total fluke that they'd met that day, that he'd ended up next to him, that they'd somehow become friends. How could anyone else ever think he, Sid Sadowskyj, the *real* Sid Sadowskyj, cowardly son, unreliable friend, eternal total fucking failure, was *great*?

Scott kneels on the floor and tries to prise Sid's hands away from his face. There is no shame in crying, he thinks. It's all part of the process for Sid, always has been. Anger, denial, tears then acceptance. He speaks softly. "You *are*, Sid. You just have this fucking cloud over your head. You think you need to fit in with other people's plans. You need to step away from whatever it is, this cloud of doubt that holds you back. You're the only one who can make that move. You're not happy. I can tell you're not happy." Scott thinks of Olsen. He'd got to know the headmaster better lately, understood now that it is fear which stops him from packing it all in and starting again, learning new languages and travelling the world. Scott leans forward, his eyes wild. "You can do it now or in thirty years, Sid. It's up to you."

Sid's shoulders heave. The tears drip onto his jeans. "I'm not *you*, Scott. I'm..."

"No better or worse."

"But I'll slow you down."

"What?" shouts Scott. "Come *on!*" He reaches out to put his hand on Sid's shoulder.

Sid bats his hand away. "Just go. Please. I'll see you at Christmas." The tears are dripping faster now, making a dark patch on his denim jeans.

"Don't get upset. There's nothing to be upset about. Just. Let's just hang out. Just be us." Scott rummages in his back pocket, finds the napkin he'd swiped from the restaurant earlier. The pattern was cool, he'd thought. He hands it to Sid. "You look like you've pissed yourself," he jokes.

Sid manages a slight smirk.

"You're a great person," says Scott. "One of my heroes."

The word sets Sid off crying again. Hero is a word neither of them use lightly. Sid looks at Scott. "I've just had a really shitty couple of weeks, you know? This place is like a fucking soap opera, I can't figure out who's on my side. I feel like everyone's talking about me." He gestures to the corridors above. "Everyone will see. I don't want them to see me like this. Scott, will you just go? Please." He puts his head in his hands again.

"Who's everyone?" asks Scott. "Who gives a shit about everyone? These people don't *know* you. This is about you and me." Scott paces up and down the kitchen. This wasn't how it was meant to go. He'd had it all planned out. He would say his speech. Sid would be suitably moved. They'd look at each other and, in that filmic

243

moment, realise that anything is possible. They'd run down the corridors to the stairwell, whooping and patting each other on the back. They'd sprint across the grass to where Scott had parked his new motorbike. Neither of them would need helmets since they both knew they were invincible. They'd roar through the city, find some rooftop bar to plot their future and the rest, as they say, would be history. Scott leans his forehead against the kitchen window and glances down at the courtyard below. "Does anyone ever go out there?" he asks.

Sid wipes his nose on his sleeve. Screw it, he's past caring about clothes. It's all just surface anyway. None of it really means anything. "Nah," he says. He closes his eyes.

It hurts Scott's heart to see Sid so despondent. If words won't work, Scott realises, he's going to have to *show* him. Give him a fucking wake-up call. Make him see that it's Scott and Sid against the world. Always has been, always will be. Desperate times call for desperate measures. He looks around the room and identifies his Plan B. Quietly, he unplugs the microwave from the wall socket.

The sound of breaking glass jolts Sid upright. The room is suddenly freezing. Scott is peering through a hole in the kitchen window the size of a TV. He turns to Sid and howls.

"Come on!" shouts Scott, tugging at Sid's shirt. He can't believe he's actually done it! "Let's go!" He is giggling, shivering in the cold. His eyes are ablaze. "Sid, come on, let's get out of here!"

Sid walks to the window. On the floors above and below, people are crowding and peering down to see what has happened. Sid's face is pale. "Are you a total idiot?" he asks Scott, mortified.

Scott surveys the damage. He watches Sid leave. Then, he closes the kitchen door behind him and walks calmly down to reception.

The security guard is looking closely at the CCTV monitor on the desk in front of him. He moves aside the silver tinsel to get a better view. "Can I help you?" he asks the boy, not looking up.

"I just smashed a window on the eighth floor," says Scott.

The security guard stares at Scott as if he is mad. Broken windows happen at least once a term. Nobody ever owns up to it.

"It was..." continues Scott. He rubs at the side of his head. "I don't know what I was thinking." He pulls his wallet out of his pocket. He'd come prepared for a night of celebrating. He counts out the notes. "Here's four hundred quid to fix it."

The security guard watches him leave. The boy is in no hurry. He walks across the grass with his head down, kicking at the turf with every fourth step. Once he is out of sight, the security guard comes to his senses, hides the money and heads upstairs to investigate.

Sid sits back in his chair, listens to the roar of the motorbike starting up in the distance, puts on his headphones and shuts his eyes.

Scott opens his front door expecting a delivery guy. He is unprepared for the sight of Sid, drenched, wearing a knitted jumper that Scott would have left in the charity shop. "I didn't think you'd actually come," Scott says, holding his arms wide.

"I'm sorry, man." Sid takes the hug.

"How long have you got?" asks Scott, breaking away.

"Nowhere else to be," says Sid with a grin.

"This is the best Christmas Eve ever!" says Sid, pressing pause on 'The Godfather' and walking across Scott's lounge to the open plan kitchen. "I feel... I dunno... different this past week. Like nothing can bring me down. I saw my mum today. She's..." He smiles.

"She's doing a bit better. Hey, I almost forgot." He reaches into his bag, brings out a stack of books, a tacky silver ribbon tied neatly around the bundle. "Call it an early Christmas present," he says, handing them to Scott.

Scott examines the titles. They are classic film text books: Deleuze, Mamet, Goldman. He's been meaning to read them forever.

"You can call it research," says Sid. "You know, for when we make our movie. That's still our plan, right?" The text message from Scott had been the peak of what was turning out to be a pretty special day. He'd been sitting on a bench in the city, watching everyone else glide sequinned and drunk from bar to bar. All it had said was two words - *Phase Three?* - but it was all Sid needed to pick up the phone and rekindle their friendship. He is desperate to know what Phase Three involves. Scott has made him wait long enough. "Let's do this properly," Sid says. "Pitch it."

Scott sits back on his sofa. With the curtains open, he can see right across the city. In the park opposite, white lights twinkle intermittently on a giant pine fir. The sky is heavy with something and he wonders if they'll wake up to snow. He folds his arms behind his head, confident and content to be back in the company of his best friend. "Can I show you yet?" he shouts across the room.

Scott's mum had popped over to see how he was getting on. She'd stacked his fridge high with Pyrex dishes and tin-foiled trays to see him through the holidays. Scott had bought her a ten-day tour around Italy, the kind of foodie holiday that Malcolm would never have been up for. It had softened the blow of telling his mum that he wouldn't be coming home on Christmas Day.

Sid microwaves two plates worth of lasagne and grabs a couple of forks from a drawer. "Come on, then," he says, setting the plates down opposite each other. He pulls two bottles of water from the fridge and places them carefully on the table. He appreciates the symmetry, the blue of the bottle and the blue of Scott's eyes, always composing photographs in his mind.

Scott finally comes out with it. "Publishing," he says. "We start a magazine company."

Sid raises his eyebrows, already dubious.

"Look," says Scott. "We already know how to make money but if we're gonna achieve our ultimate aim..." He smacks his palm on the table and waits for Sid to fill in the gap.

"Make a movie?" offers Sid.

"Make a movie, exactly," says Scott. "Then we need to know the ins and outs of running a company. Production, post and distribution. Images."

"Agreed," says Sid through a mouthful of lasagne. "Why don't we just start a film company? I know this film student at uni, she could..."

"It's too early for that. We've got no experience in the film industry." Scott shakes his head. He's considered it, of course, but he is almost certain that, in film, you only get one chance to make it work. "If we bombed, then what? No," says Scott with confidence. "We learn our trade in a different industry. We don't want to look like amateurs. Trust me, I've done my research."

It makes sense so far, thinks Sid. Just one minor issue. "How are we going to pay for it?"

"Do you have any savings left?"

Sid shakes his head. "I spent most of it. Uni fees and mum's rehab. What about you?"

"I'll figure it out, says Scott, vaguely. Truth is, he's spent most of his money on his flat. No expense spared and it shows. He'd figured he could always make more, that he might as well enjoy what he had, that there was no point in stashing it away. There was also the small matter of the vintage camera he'd bought Sid for Christmas, which wasn't as cheap as it should have been. "Leave it with me," he reassures Sid, hoping he sounds more confident than he feels. There's no point troubling Sid at this point. Nah, thinks Scott, it'll be fine. He'll find a way. He always does.

Sid flicks through the collages that Scott has compiled. "So, you're gonna quit your job?"

"Not yet," says Scott, "but you should quit uni."

Sid clatters his fork onto his plate. "What, you don't quit your job but I quit uni?" He looks sceptical.

Scott is prepared. He holds up his hands in surrender. "I can print all our sales and marketing material at the school. If I quit now, we'll have to pay for all that print. I can get all the contract forms and flyers done there. Plus, my job gives us a bit of money to live off."

Sid weighs it up. What the hell, he'd been ready to quit uni anyway. There'd been so many times that first term when he'd looked up, certain he could sense Scott sitting behind him in the lecture theatre, judging him. It put him on edge. He'd tried to love uni, thrown himself into every social event. He was never short of people to go drinking with. But Scott had been right. It wasn't enough. "So, what's our next step?"

Scott beams. "I've got work experience at the city's largest newspaper and…"

"What! How did you manage that?"

Scott stares at him as though it is obvious. "I photocopied the work experience form at school and sent it out. I'll learn as much as I can from them."

"Boom!" says Sid, polishing off the rest of his meal.

"Easy peasy," laughs Scott. He gives Sid a sly smile. "You didn't think I'd work for Olsen and not find a way to screw him over, did you?"

Sid laughs. "We start tomorrow."

CHAPTER 23

"Think that's the last of it," says Scott, happy to be completing what he considers the most important task in Sid's commitment to their friendship. As long as Sid still had that bedroom at uni, he couldn't possibly begin to re-build his life. Helping him move feels like an exorcism of sorts. Should've brought a crucifix, Scott thinks with a grin. Really freaked Reashan out. Scott's glad that Sid couldn't make it in the end. He couldn't handle a U-turn now, not now they've finally found common ground again.

"Careful with that one," Scott says as he hands the final cardboard box to Reashan. It's full of Sid's favourite things. The Dreamchasers list has been ironed flat, put inside a plastic folder, a layer of bubble-wrap around that. Scott's curiosity had got the better of him and he'd peeked, got a lump in his throat when he saw what it was.

Reashan gently wedges his mate's possessions beside his own in the back of the van. He's glad to be helping out, still feels like he owes the pair of them, if he's honest. Plus, if he's being completely truthful, he wants to show off a bit. Scott's always been impossible to impress and Reashan's van is about the only thing in his life that he's proud of. Properly proud of. The only thing he's ever made that

Leila looks at and knows she couldn't have done better. The van is nearly finished. The design didn't lend itself easily to adaptation, not like the VW campers he'd seen online. But it was his and he'd made the most of it. A single mattress covers the floor, and he'd managed to sleep more soundly, curled around the spare wheel, than he had for years in his own bed.

Scott answers his phone as Reashan slams the van doors shut. "Sid, hey," he says. "Yep, we're just heading back now. Nah, we didn't see anyone, no one asked any questions. Yeah, see you soon. Yep. Yeah the room's totally empty…" Scott rolls his eyes at Reashan. "Yes, I hoovered." He puts a finger to his lips, tells Reashan to ssshh-our-little-secret. "Yep. Bye Sid, bye." Scott shoves his phone into his hoodie pocket and turns the radio dials on the dashboard.

"Dunno if that'll work," says Reashan. "I've just been using CDs."

The neon of a fast-food drive-thru looms ahead. "You hungry?" asks Scott. "My shout."

Reashan drives straight passed the turning. "I'm trying to stay fit," he says.

Scott frowns. He could've murdered a burger. Whatever. Driver's rules. "You're looking great," he tells Reashan. It's true. Reashan had lost the watery glaze to his eyes that he'd always had. It's impressive, thinks Scott, the ability of the human body to mend and re-invent itself, rid itself of the characteristics we consider ingrained. Reashan has grown his hair, too. Scott had always considered his crew cut as a kind of fuck-you to his dad, who, Scott's pretty sure, would have trained his kids to be the Asian White Stripes if he'd had his way. They seemed to have a love/hate thing going on; Reashan and his dad. Scott has a fleeting vision of Malcolm and laughs out loud. First time he's thought of his *own* dad since he walked out three years ago. Says it all.

Reashan glances at Scott. He wishes he could say the same, but

251

Scott still looks exactly the same. A total mess. "Must be good to have Sid back again."

Scott frowns. "Don't get too used to it," he says without thinking. "I'm still not totally convinced."

Reashan keeps his eyes on the road. "You just have to find a way to convince him that he's studying. Even if it's at the university of life or whatever they call it. That he's bettering himself somehow." He laughs. "Me, I always hated that shit. But Sid, give him a timetable, a clipboard and a spreadsheet and he'll stick at it for years. That's what always worked about you guys. You fit around each other. You fill in the other's blanks. You know?"

Those words were the most true Scott has heard from anyone in months. He'd never realised Reashan was so perceptive.

"How you finding the money for this magazine anyway?" Reashan asks. "I'd lend you some but I'm pretty much hand-to-mouth these days. Gotta make this month-off count. Then it's back to the cleaning business."

"The money? If I told you that, I'd have to kill you," Scott jokes. He changes the subject. "Where you heading, anyway?"

"Leaving for Berlin tomorrow."

"Long drive."

"Fuck yeah. Seriously though, Scott. Can't be cheap. That office and all the gear and all that."

Scott drums his fingers against the dashboard as a beat takes hold in his head. "Yeah well, my rent's cheap and Sid's back at his mum's so. Don't worry, I got this," he says. "I did what I had to do."

CHAPTER 24

Software, design, printing, delivery. They knew nothing about any of it. But it was pictures, stories, one step closer towards writing a film. Sid approaches the task with his usual perfection. He even adopts a uniform. Crisp Oxford shirt, says he has to look the part. The huge office space is all theirs, flooded with sunlight on the third floor, right near the river. They'd tried sitting at opposite ends, but Sid had been too wound up by Scott's habit of launching his bouncy ball the length of the room, avoiding the concrete pillars holding up the roof. Sid had moved their desks, first thing, one morning. Dragged Scott's and plonked it down a metre or so from his, so he can keep an eye on him. The only rubbish on Sid's desk is the tiny discs of paper produced by the hole punch, and even that is emptied hourly. Scott's desk is like everything he owns, a fuck-you to conformity. The contents of the bin spill out onto the floor, there's a cup of coffee too close to the sockets. The notes stickered to the desk, which to the passing observer might look like the fruit of a hard day's labour, reveal themselves to be scribbles about cinema times, lines from movies, Scott's requests for snacks. A globe sits on top of his notebook, covered in stickers marking places on his visit wish-list.

Sid knows things are bad when Scott's bouncing his ball at that speed. He can see it moving in his peripheral vision. A hummingbird, trapped in a glass box, starting to wonder if it'll ever get out alive. Sid stops what he's doing. "What's wrong, Scott? You seem a bit… jittery."

"Nothing," says Scott, swivelling around in his chair.

Sid doesn't have time for this. There's still seventy emails to send today. He's trying to make them all personal, do a little research on the background of each company before he dives straight in and asks them to advertise. He's not up for another all-nighter. "I can tell when something's wrong. You know I can."

Scott laughs like a maniac.

Sid doesn't get what's funny. "What is it?"

"It's just tough," says Scott. "I mean…"

"… yeah it is. But we're getting there, we're doing it."

"How many sales have we got now?"

Sid taps on the keyboard. "316 before profit."

"No, *now*," repeats Scott. "How many sales do we have now?"

"Er, what?" Sid doesn't get the urgency. They've been working with these numbers all day. Scott's been there in the room with him, right in his goddamn ear the whole time he's been making the calls, telling him what to say, what not to say, how to say it better next time.

Scott loses it. "How many sales do we have *now*?" he shouts.

Scrolling through the spreadsheet, Sid answers quietly. "Seven."

"Seven?" The bouncy ball begins its beat again.

"It's fine," soothes Sid. It really is. Everything's going to plan.

"OK… how long til we break even? How many?"

"316."

"And how long will that take?"

Sid takes his time. "I reckon about… maybe three editions but that's… that's normal."

"Three editions. That's… three months…"

"Maybe a bit more." Always better to err on the side of caution, thinks Sid.

"… that's a hundred grand." Scott misses his catch.

"What did you say?" Sid's really confused now. Scott's crap with numbers, Sid's always known that, but still. His expression tells Sid it's more than just that. "A hundred grand?"

Scott is silent.

"Scott? Scott! Where did you get that figure from? It's not a hundred grand."

Scott throws the ball at Sid's table and grabs his coat, leaving a trail of paper between him and a bewildered Sid. "I'll be back," he shouts, crashing through the doors and racing down the stairs.

Scott curls up in his swivel chair and looks out over the horizon. "Crap," he says out loud. "Crap, crap, crap, crap, FUCK." He throws his bouncy ball hard against the toughened glass. The room seems to mock Scott now. He'd paid three months' rent upfront, in cash, wholeheartedly optimistic (crushingly naïve, he sees now), thinking that by now the place would be buzzing with employees, that they'd at least be breaking even. Sid's desk takes pride of place, his piles of paperwork and folders neatly ordered. He's put everything into this. "Crap," Scott says again. He pulls his T-shirt up over his head, wanting to hide. He can't believe what an idiot he's been. The page in front of him is covered with scribbles. The numbers are doing his head in. No matter which way he looks at them, the sums just don't add up. There's no getting around it.

He resents it, a little. The fact that he's always expected to bail them out of trouble. The way Sid would sit back and wait for him to mastermind the next move. Sometimes, Scott wishes he could flick the switch to cruise control, leave it all to fate. No. He snaps his notebook closed, gets to his feet, his mind racing to figure out how to break it to Sid. It'll be Game Over.

It feels like it will never end. Twenty minutes so far and Sid is still launching himself at him, Scott sitting with his back against a metal girder in the middle of the room, wishing he hadn't said anything.

"How can you be so stupid and fucking ruin everything before we have even started? Scott…tell me, fucking tell me!" screams Sid. He's kicking at the boxes, screaming into Scott's face. "Fucking answer me!"

"Look it was a long shot, OK?" Scott screams back, wishing the box wasn't taking the hit, wanting Sid to cross the line, to draw blood. He deserves it. "I fucked up." It hurts to admit it.

Sid's voice is breaking. "You're a fucking idiot, Scott!" He takes another run, wanting to keep going, to pummel Scott against the steel. "You set us up to fail before we even started!" He counts all the sacrifices he's made for Scott. "I had so much on this and I can't fucking do it anymore." Sid is pacing, ranting, so far removed from himself that he's worried what he'll do next. This isn't him. "I should've listened to Mr Olsen when I was at school and he told me. You are a dreamer, Scott, you know what." He spits out the words. "You're a fucking dreamer."

The words hurt more than a hit ever could. Scott struggles to defend himself. He sits and takes it.

There's no filter on him. Just words and hate and Sid's reeling with the pain of it all. "I had so much going for me, Scott!" he screams. "At school and… I had so much planned ahead a-a-and university, and you. You took it all away from me." He launches a box at Scott's head. "I threw it all away for you."

Sid takes a breath, waits for Scott to make it better. To say the words that'll fix it. Fucking nothing. Sid visualises the greasy spoon where it went down - Scott sitting with the Watson Brothers, casually pissing away his future, signing their death warrant, while Nicky fucking Watson takes a slurp of fucking hot chocolate. The venom tumbles from his tongue, more poisonous than before. "How could you be so fucking stupid? Fucking dealing with those guys again. I'm not running from those meatheads *again*. Why didn't you just tell me you didn't have any money?"

Nothing.

He screams into Scott's face. "I said why didn't you tell me?"

"It's because I couldn't! Don't you get that I can't do any of this without you?"

"You can't do anything without me." Sid scoffs. "Or on your own. You're useless."

Scott bows his head.

"And you're fucked now because I'm not staying with you anymore. I can't do it anymore." He takes a final run at Scott, stops an inch away from Scott's face. "I can't deal with it anymore!" His heart is already out the door, chasing itself in circles through the backstreets, like he's a scared little kid again, trying to remember how to breathe, how to be human. "Find someone else to be your fucking little... rat."

After he's gone, Scott sits until the windows blacken, not giving a shit that every office block around them can see him there, knees drawn up to his chest under the fluorescent strip-lights, his T-shirt soaked from tears, glad for the pillar to stop him from dissolving into the floor.

When Sid finally makes it home, he is ready for bed. He and his mum are co-existing in a sense of semi-normality at the moment.

Tossing his keys on the kitchen counter, he is relieved to see that the dishes have been done. A pair of pink rubber gloves are hanging to dry beside the clean dishes. Sid smiles. It's the work of a sober person. "Hi, ma," he shouts through to the living room. After years of tiptoeing around each other, Karen and Sid have finally found the confidence to try out new phrases. "Ma" is Karen's current favourite. Sid uses it whenever he remembers.

Karen pushes open the door to the living room, proud of herself. "I made us some pizza."

Sid is impressed. "You made pizza?"

She points at the small table in the living room. The baking tray is placed on an old trivet so as not to mark the wood, and the pizza is burnt at the edges. She pulls a gooey slice and hands it to her son.

Sid beams. "Thanks." He wolfs it down, not minding that pizza is all he's eaten today or that, without a plate, the grease gets everywhere. It is the best pizza he's ever eaten. "Mum."

Karen looks up from her own slice, oblivious to the effect her minimal effort at cooking has had on her son. She'd wanted to make some proper food for him. Start to pay back all those years he'd looked after her.

Sid sits down next to her. He wants to tell his mum everything, to ask for advice and get it. But telling her about his argument with Scott would mean laying bare all the details: the Watson Brothers, the web that had been spun around him. His mum's role in all of it. It is better for both of them if they don't dwell on the past. It's taken long enough just to reach this point, where they can sit on the sofa and eat a pizza together. "Just...give us a hug, ma."

Karen looks at her son with more lucidity than Sid has ever seen in her eyes. "You're a kind soul, son," she says. "Don't underestimate how important that is." She is suddenly serious. "Listen. I need to tell you something."

Sid turns off the TV.

Karen searches for her voice. It had been part of the plan. The pizza, the washing up... she wants to show her son how much she has changed. She shouldn't still be keeping secrets from him. "Your dad," she begins. She manages to say his name. "Lucasz. I always told you that he left us when you were a baby."

Sid frowns. He's never heard her say his name before.

"Son, I found your letters. I'm sorry, I didn't read them all, but I was looking for some old photos of my mum's and I saw the guitar case under your bed and I just..." She smiles. "That's how I remember your dad, you know. Up on stage, playing guitar. I just wanted to check that it really had gone, that I didn't imagine seeing it in a pawn shop all those years ago."

Sid wonders what she's getting at. He'd forgotten about the letters. Can't even remember the day when he'd written the last one. She can burn them for all he cares. Everything that's in them, Sid's said to her now. But there's something else, he can tell. It's not about the letters. His mum is fiddling with her hands, won't look him in the eye.

"Your dad didn't leave us, Sid. I left him. He wanted so bad to be part of your life and I cut him out." She picks at the skin around her painted fingernails. "I couldn't handle being that close to someone. I shouldn't have lied to you. You know, son." She holds out her hand for Sid to take. "The ones who make us feel alive, make us recognise something terrifying and beautiful about ourselves. They lead us to the edge of the water and we get too scared to jump in. We always hurt the people we love most."

CHAPTER 25

Scott skulks into the room. Sid's acting as if nothing has changed. He's tidied up, put all the boxes back where they belong. Scott's bouncy ball is sitting neatly on his desk. Scott walks slowly, checking the ground beneath him for landmines. "Sid." He takes a few cautiously steps towards him. "My best mate."

The words "Operation: ELSA FURY" are written in Sid's neat handwriting on the flip-chart. Sid crosses the room and fiddles with the blinds and then the window, trying to find some air. He takes a deep breath. "Wait," he warns. Sid knows what his friend is like; one false move and Scott will head for the door. It has to be pitch perfect this time. Sid has to make it count. Standing there, in his ironed white shirt and navy trousers, he's transported back five years to the first day they met, anxious to lay his cards on the table, terrified that they would be rejected. He suddenly feels nervous.

Scott obeys. He is feeling a little apprehensive around his friend. Sid's change of heart had been sudden and unexpected. It was as though something had finally clicked, and Sid not only had confidence in himself but he had managed to forgive Scott his shortcomings. Standing here now, it's clear that Sid is a force to be reckoned with.

"On this board is the solution to our problem. It's gonna kill us, trying to get there. But." He seeks out Scott's eyes, waits for his mate to look up. "I'm willing to give it a go if you are." His tone changes. "Subject to a few new ground rules."

"Whatever you want, Sid. I'm all..."

Sid interrupts. "Never, ever, *ever*." He pauses for breath. "Lie to me again."

Scott crosses his heart. "I won't. I promise. I know I messed up. I won't."

"I want full and frank disclosure from now on. We've always said it's fifty-fifty and the problems are the same."

Scott feels his eyes begin to well up, and for once he isn't afraid to let Sid see. He doesn't turn away. "I'm sorry."

Sid's face softens. God, he hopes he doesn't cry. Sid's had his fill of crying for one week. He just wants to get on with it. He hopes he looks better than he feels. He'd been up half the night talking with his mum, then spent a good few hours hating everyone and everything. It was only at three that he'd dragged his sorry self out of bed and got his priorities straight. His head is killing him. There were no painkillers at his mum's house. No tablets of any sort, just in case. He keeps it together, just.

"You're my hero, ain't you." Scott says it brusquely, winking to make Sid smile, not wanting to embarrass his friend any more than strictly necessary. Most people wouldn't have given Scott a second chance. But then Sid Sadowskyj isn't most people. "So, show me this masterplan, then." He wipes the back of his sleeve across his cheeks and sits down.

Sid clears his throat. "Elsa. Elliott Sadowskyj. Fury. We just fucking go at it, all out. A thirty-day sales blitz. Intense sales. Outsourcing. We come away at the end of thirty days with all debts resolved. All ties with the Watson Brothers severed." He widens his eyes at Scott to make sure he gets the point. "For good. Any objections so far?"

Scott shakes his head.

"So we carry on with the magazine," continues Sid. "But big time. Text, images, logo, designs, photography, graphics, even videos. We branch out online, website design, SEO, the works. We do everything. Except we don't. We stop fannying around trying to do everything ourselves and we find a bunch of specialists who can make everything look as slick as possible. Make it seamless. We go in with the big guns. We don't just feature small businesses, we approach the big players as equals. We act as their marketing department. You know what they're like, the Council, the banks... shit, anywhere where there's an executive involved. They don't have a clue. They're throwing money away. Just one problem. We only have thirty days. We can't handle all the work ourselves. There's just not enough time."

Scott smiles. The whole plan sounds like something he could have written himself. He agrees with every word. If they're ever to achieve their ultimate aim - and isn't that the whole point, to make a movie before they're thirty - he needs more space to focus. Walks alone and nights by himself are few and far between these days and he can feel it all slipping away from his grasp. Control. It's about the only thing he really needs. He watches Sid turn the page, constantly amazed by his friend's ability to shed his nerves and assume the necessary role. "You really think we can make it work? I mean, shit, Sid... *I'm* meant to be the optimistic one."

"Dream big," says Sid, batting off Scott's incredulity. "Why not? You once said to me that if someone else can do it, then why not us? Why not me? And if it hasn't been done, it's just because the right person hasn't come along to do it." He smiles at Scott. "So, what's the problem?"

"No problem," says Scott. "Easy peasy." He watches Sid's face as he carries on with the pitch. Over the years, Sid has lost his vulnerable look, the out-of-timeness that made strangers ask what the deal was with him. Now, though, as Sid stands facing Scott and holds his gaze, the eagerness to please is back. His eyes give Scott no option but to agree. He can't deny that there is something thrilling about the prospect of the challenge. The fierce glimmer in Sid's eyes isn't about to fade any time soon. "How about we offer a one-off fee to feature in the magazine," Scott suggests. "Build up their trust and prove to them how good we are. We could offer our services on a monthly retainer. Become a marketing department plug-in!"

"Boom," shouts Sid. "Chuck us the ball."

Scott rolls the ball across the table to Sid, who is about to bounce it when Scott has a thought. "But we can't design websites and we don't know about marketing or design."

"I don't want to know how to design sites," says Sid. "Do you?"

"No," says Scott.

Sid scoffs. "Does Tarantino act?"

"Well, yeah actually..." says Scott.

"OK, bad example," concedes Sid. "All I mean is this. We are producers. We're the relationship-makers. All we do is marry the clients with the designers and the photographers. We get the sale and then get some other guys to do the job. We oversee it. Produce it. Easy."

"Who's gonna help us?"

"Well," says Sid. "The most reliable workforce we know currently work for Reashan and the cleaning business. But, from what I hear, they *are* looking for more work."

"So," suggests Scott. "They work nights?"

Sid shoots him down. "No, Scott, they can't work nights, they're the main business. They can't work nights, they've gotta work full time with us. They'll be our sales team for now, and that means they've gotta be in the office for business hours. "

"How's that gonna work?"

Sid has it all figured out. "Reashan carries on with the cleaning business, gives us some staff in return for shares."

"Sweet! Indian outsourcing!"

Sid cringes, glad they're alone in the room. "You can't say that."

"No?" Scott can tell by Sid's face that he's crossed a line. Stuff just tumbles out sometimes, he can't help himself.

"No." Sid whispers. "It's not PC."

"I'll just think it then."

"Keep it in your head."

"I will."

"You do that." Christ, thinks Sid, he's from another planet sometimes.

Scott smirks. Anything to stop the ice from thawing over their heads again.

Sid remembers his train of thought. "We are outsourcing, though. All the designs go to Mumbai to be finished."

"Reashan's cousins?"

"Exactly. They know what they're doing and they've agreed to be paid on a rolling contract. We give our clients over here the capabilities of an in-house marketing department and design department without the in-house cost. Obviously, we'll need people on the ground here too. Designers, copywriters, photographers. We'll try the media courses at uni. Everyone's looking to put together a portfolio. They'll be happy for the experience."

Scott admires the genius of Sid's plan. He's thought of every detail. "We're the producers, the directors. We're a step closer to movies." He is grinning now. "It's perfect. I *love* it."

"Scott. This is a fire-fighting plan. It's got to work. We spend nothing, we save up and we pay them back. Then we grow."

Scott can't stand the seriousness. It still makes him feel sick to have let Sid down. It feels like Elsa Fury is the equivalent of the two of them running at full pelt towards the edge of a massive crevasse; sharks circling in the water below and wolves closing in behind. They have no option but to grab hold of each other and leap. Like Thelma and Louise, without the headscarves or the death wish. "Sidney," Scott smiles. "If you were a woman."

Sid throws his marker pen at Scott's head. "Dirty bastard," he laughs. "Hey. Just one last thing. What about the Watson Brothers? If this has any chance of working, you've gotta get them off our back for a month."

"Don't worry about them," says Scott, a sly smile forming at the corner of his mouth. "I've arranged a meeting this Friday. I'm gonna watch 'The Godfather'. I'll sort it."

"You know," says Scott, looking up from his computer. Reashan left an hour ago, desperate to get stuck into his new responsibilities, happy to be included in the plan. He'd screeched off in his van, but Leila had asked if she could stay. She's sitting on the sofa, flicking robotically through the TV channels. Scott's whole flat smells of the nail varnish she's spent half an hour applying in precise strokes. Scott's been vaguely aware of her talking the whole time. He glances at Sid. Sid is pretending to be interested, eyes fixed on his notes with an intense frown, placating Leila with the occasional kind word. Scott can't take it any longer. "Leila, you spend so long moaning about what you don't want to do. What is it that you actually *want?*"

Sid shifts uncomfortably in his seat. "Jesus, Scott, don't hold back," he mutters. He tops up Leila's glass with wine.

"I'm serious." Scott moves Leila's legs unceremoniously out of the way and sinks down beside her into the sofa. "You sit in the park all day with your textbooks but you hate your course at uni. You say you want to go on holiday but you're afraid to get on a plane. You say your brother has it easy but you were both born on the same day, in the same place, within minutes of each other. You say you need a job but you'd rather do something menial than start something that actually interests you." Scott can sense Leila's eyes boring holes in his skull but he doesn't let it stop him. "I think you make excuses."

Sid backs away. At times, Scott and Leila make him feel like a wounded peacekeeper in a besieged war-zone. They're as bad as each other. He puts down his pen. "Anyone want a cup of tea?"

Leila snaps at Scott. "You think I make excuses?"

Sid flicks the kettle switch, busies himself clattering around in the cupboards. Goddamn open plan living, he thinks. He can still hear every word.

"All I'm saying," answers Scott, unscrewing the lid from Leila's bottle of nail varnish, "is that a change might do you good."

Leila simmers silently in the seat next to him.

The kettle flicks off. Sid hums loudly, taking himself out of the equation.

Unperturbed, Scott begins to painstakingly paint his thumb nail. He's fed up of tiptoeing around Leila, watching her wallow. She's one of the good ones. She deserves to be happy.

Leila watches Scott carefully. He's so fucking weird, she thinks. But he's got a point. That's the thing about Scott. He says what everybody else is thinking. She tries to get over herself. Eventually, the sight of four red nails on Scott's hand makes her laugh out loud.

"See!" Scott reaches over and elbows her gently. "That's what I'm talking about. We've missed your smile."

"You're a bastard," she says.

Sensing that the bomb has been de-fused, Sid re-appears from the kitchen with three mugs of tea, swipes his notebook from the table on his way to the sofa. "So." He hands a cup to Leila. Black tea, two sugars, just the way she likes it. He flashes his best grin. "When do you start?"

Leila looks from Sid to Scott and back again. She narrows her eyes. "You two planned this, didn't you?"

"Perhaps," says Scott.

"Maybe a little. Seriously though, Leila, we need someone we can trust to run the office."

"Someone smart," says Scott.

"Someone responsible," adds Sid.

"Someone who'll work for free?" guesses Leila.

"For now," Scott says. "But c'mon, you know us. You know we won't rip you off."

Leila thinks it over. To be honest, it's the best offer she's had in months. She'd been silently seething when they'd given the recruitment job to Reashan, told him what would be in it for him. She'd sat next to him on the sofa, feeling invisible, another chalk mark to her brother in their never-ending, lifelong game of one-upmanship. If it doesn't work out, so what, it's only thirty days. Might as well give it a shot. Nothing to lose. "You know you two are impossible to say no to."

"Will this do?" she asks the following morning, leaning against the doorframe of Scott's office.

Scott looks her up and down. The trouser suit is a welcome change from the old band T-shirt and ripped jeans she usually wears. Her silver nose ring has gone and a bright blue stud glistens in its place. She's even done something different with her hair: two precise plaits cross over the crown of her head. "You look…"

Scott hesitates.

"Professional?" she offers. "That's what I was going for."

"You look cool as fuck," Sid bellows from the end of the corridor. He wraps his arm around Scott's shoulder. "Let's do this thing. The first lot are here."

"OK." Scott claps his hands. "Leila, before we get started, I want you to go down there and round up anyone who's smoking or who smells like they've even been in contact with a cigarette. Send them home."

"No smokers?" Sid looks unsure. "Can we do that?"

Leila pulls a half-smoked packet of Camels from her bag. "Yeah, I mean... it seems a little hypocritical." Growing up with free access to a tobacco counter had its benefits. She hates herself for doing it but it's a hard habit to kick. She shakes the packet at Scott.

"That's different," Scott winks. "You're management."

"Besides," says Sid. "We've seen what you're like when you go all day without one. Wouldn't wish that on anyone. Just be discreet."

Leila nods.

"Look," says Scott, gearing himself up for the first round of interviews. "It's gonna be hard work. We don't want our staff taking fag breaks every ten minutes."

"What do I say to them?" asks Leila.

Scott thinks on his feet. "Health and safety?"

CHAPTER 26

After two days of careful scrutiny, they have assembled a team of workers with enough enthusiasm, blind faith and energy to face the feat ahead. Another two days and they have ironed out technical issues and fine-tuned their protocols, so that Scott and Sid feel confident that they can handle any challenges that the next month might throw at them. They are optimistic. It is the only way to be.

Scott and Sid stand on the balcony above the sales floor and eye up their recruits. Some faces they recognise from school, others from interviews that had bordered on interrogation. It had always been Sid's forté, organising appointments, calculating risk, assessing potential. He has an eye for the outsider, the over-achiever, the quiet, clever ones, the ones that slip under the radar. He has a gentleness that coaxes people out of their shells and lets them know he's one of them. He'd had no trouble getting people to join them. Scott, meanwhile, had taken a less conventional route. He'd spent a day in The Shambles, accosting anyone who showed a glimmer of rebellion, his boots pounding the cobbles in pursuit, recruiting comrades like a deranged cult leader. It had worked.

Cans of Red Bull and bottles of water are stacked beside every phone. Leila has strategically placed water urns and industrial-strength pots of coffee around the office, so it is only a few steps in any direction to the nearest caffeine fix. After careful research about the best plants to stimulate productivity, she's dotted the room with Peace Lilies. Scott loves this touch: it reminds him of Leon up on the big screen, carefully tending to his beloved Peace Lily that basks in the Bronx sunlight as his world caves in. At either side of the room, long tables are laid out with fresh fruit and sandwich platters. The hours these kids are about to put in, they'll feel as though they haven't seen daylight in weeks. Scott and Sid want them to feel as looked-after as possible. The last thing they need now is quitters.

Scott and Sid look at each other. The blue war paint had been Sid's idea, an homage to the greats. This is their Bannockburn. It is do or die.

"You ready?" asks Scott, the paint cracking around his mouth when he gives a slight smile.

Sid pushes away from the balcony and they advance down to the main floor.

The room hushes at the sight of them, coffee cups placed silently back onto the tables. Leila tucks her hair behind her ears and flicks up the collar on her leather jacket, proud to be part of it.

Scott takes his place at the front. Two hundred faces look back at him, painted blue just like his own, the war stripes uniting the crowd before he's even said a word. "Ladies and gentlemen," he yells.

Sid smiles. Scott can turn on the charm when he wants to. Standing up there in front of their army, posture-perfect with a clean suit on, Scott looks a million miles away from the shambolic zombie he'd encountered in the kitchen this morning. They hadn't slept. It'd taken four cups of coffee to even get Scott out of the door.

Sid stands tall beside him. The petrol blue suit he has chosen is slick, his shoes polished. Though Scott is the mouthpiece, most eyes are on him. He seems oblivious. He focuses at a point on the far wall and listens intently, waiting for his cue.

Scott looks out at his comrades. "There's a quote. From Shakespeare's 'Twelfth Night'." He begins to pace. "And it's been with me in my head for years. And whenever I have a pen in my hand, I'm always writing it down." He pauses for effect, glances at Sid. "Be not afraid of greatness. Some are born great. Some *achieve* greatness. And others have greatness *thrust* upon them."

The room is silent.

He throws out his palm towards Sid. "This is my best mate," he says proudly. "You see, I messed up. I messed something up between us. I took our relationship for granted and *fucked it up*." He is angry at himself, at the memory of his betrayal, his voice catching in his throat. "I thought I was doing something for us. When really I was doing it for me."

Sid's bottom lip trembles at Scott's confession, and he's glad for the paint on his face, warping his features so that no one can tell.

Scott is staring at him. "My mind isn't good enough without *his* mind. And what I took for granted was how much he gave me."

Sid takes a sharp intake of breath.

Scott addresses the room. "Now, when you leave here today, I want you to do one thing. I want you to look up at the sky. Because there's someone, somewhere else, looking up at that same sky and they do not *have* the choice you have. You know, after we have our freedom, I believe we have a responsibility to dream. You know, to look up and to say, 'What's next?' To *dare*... to be great. I need you to help me. We ain't fighting no war. We're not fighting for our lives. And you might not even be fighting for your dreams. But I *need* you to help me fight for *mine*. Because this *is* a war, for us." Scott stops moving, stands face-on so they can all see him, see how much it means to be part of this. "Because you have your *freedom* now." He feels the beat of his favourite song pounding at his temples. "Will you go out and chase your dreams?" He can hear the blood whooshing around his skull, wonders if Sid's feeling the same rush. "Will you help me chase mine?"

Sid feels the baton pass from his friend to him, he can't stand there in silence anymore. He raises his fist, fills his lungs with air and screams his war cry. Failure is not an option.

Three weeks later, Sid is sitting nervously at his desk, in his office on the top floor, waiting for the thump of Scott's boots bounding up the stairs. He keeps checking his phone. He's turned it up to the loudest setting, fully expecting that any second now, the police will call to ask him to identify his friend's body. Sid had refused to go along, not wanting to be anywhere near the Watson Brothers. Now, he's convinced himself he's fed Scott to the wolves.

Scott finally makes an appearance.

"How'd it go?" asks Sid, knocking over his chair as he gets up to greet him.

"Better than expected," jokes Scott.

"That's it then, yeah? We're clear? No more debt? You get it in writing?"

Scott hands Sid the contract. The signatories are blank. "Don't think Gavin even knows how to write his name."

"But we're good though, yeah?" asks Sid. "We can put all this shit behind us?"

Scott halts in his step, narrows his eyes. "There's just one tiny little detail."

"What?"

"They did... they did threaten to burn down our offices."

Sid asks him to repeat it. He hears the buzz of the sales team on the floor above, the whirr of roller-skating receptionists around the office, the hum of real people who have stepped up for them, whose livelihoods they are responsible for. He stands up, looks out of the window, tries to remember what kind of car the Watsons drive.

"Come on, man!" Scott tries to reassure him. "It's just bravado. You don't think they'd actually do it? Do you?"

Sid is glaring at Scott like he's a total idiot.

"Nah, you're right," says Scott. "Best not risk it, eh?"

"Call everyone who's not here. Get them in. We're moving tonight." Sid begins to gather his belongings together, grabs the empty storage boxes from the filing cabinet behind him. This is it, he promises himself. The last roll of the dice in this game of snakes and ladders. "Scott! What you doing?"

Scott is taking enormous bites from a burger. He's picked out the slice of gherkin, tries to fling it into the bin and misses.

"Seriously? You stopped to get food on the way? I thought you were lying in a ditch."

"What? I was hungry!" Scott crams the last of the burger into his mouth. "Hey, you know who else we should call. Remember that detective? He'd love a shot at the Watson Brothers. You know, just in case they do turn up with their lighter fluid, figure out how to strike a match. They'll have a little welcome committee."

CHAPTER 27

Sid parks his Porsche in the same spot as always, a bay marked 'Executive' just next to the main door. It had taken him a while to get used to the word. He grabs the tray of coffees from the passenger seat. Usually, he makes a habit of getting in to work at seven, but the party last night had gone on into the small hours and he'd appreciated the extra hour in bed. He feels a little worse for wear, tired mainly, but it is nothing he can't handle.

"Morning," he chirps, handing out coffees as he walks through the offices. The whole building is theirs now. Three stories of modernist glass and steel, way better than the original place. First class conference facilities. There is even a sofa bed in one of the rooms, for those nights between big meetings when it isn't worth going home. Best of all, the sign emblazoned on the side of the building says 'Elsa Media'. He and Scott are equals.

Sid knocks on Scott's office and walks straight in. He shouts his friend's name four times before Scott looks up.

"Last night was something else," he says, passing a cappuccino to Scott and hanging up his coat on the back of the door.

Scott's smile is weak.

"What's up with you?"

"Nothing," says Scott. "Just thinking."

Sid grins. "You're always thinking. What is it?"

Scott frowns at him. "I saw Shane Lawson in the supermarket."

"Oh. Right," says Sid. He checks his phone and smiles. He'd won a bet from last night and he'd saved the evidence as his screensaver to prove it. "Lunch at two?" he asks Scott. He scans his friend's desk. A mess, as usual. Sid sometimes wonders how Scott ever gets any work done, yet he is the most productive person Sid knows. He spots a bouncy ball amidst the chaos and passes it to Scott.

"Make it half one and I'm in," suggests Scott, catching the ball easily.

"Deal." Sid turns to leave.

Scott can hear them out in the offices, the inane chatter of a dozen voices and Sid's clear above it all, congratulating, encouraging, respectful and respected. He shuffles down in his chair, failing to make himself comfortable, and reads the words on the screen over and over. He can't think straight this morning. A minute later, he stops and presses Delete until the words are erased. The whole week has felt like a process of erasure. His meeting with Shane had disorientated him, like a blizzard that ambushed from every direction and left him afraid to look up. It was as though his compass had been scrambled. He can't figure out which way is up. He tilts his head to one side and begins to type again.

Sid looks up from his work and sees Scott through the glass panel. Scott's face is pale. In the light, with the blue grid of the glass against his profile, he looks like a computer-generated image, mid-design. He is muttering to himself. He takes too long to open the door, as though he's building up to something. Sid braces himself.

"Hi," says Scott when he's at the desk, as though only just noticing Sid. To Scott, Sid's desk always appears too neat to be functional. Even the arrangement of quickly-scribbled post-it notes looks orchestrated, stuck in a straight horizontal line near the computer in order of priority.

"Hey," says Sid, not looking up.

"So, I was in the supermarket the other week and saw Shane."

Sid continues to type. "Yeah, you said."

The wind blasts at the windows, making the glass whine. "Talking about work, girlfriends, y'know, small talk. Then. I just said goodbye, walked off."

There's a storm forecast. Sid wants to get away. He flashes him a look. "I'm actually a bit busy, Scott..."

"Hold on," interrupts Scott. "And when I walked away I rushed to my car, parked outside the supermarket and waited a couple of minutes for Shane to walk out. He came out and I waved at him and drove off."

Sid sighs. "As interesting as this story is, I'm trying to work."

"I wanted to show off," Scott admits.

Sid leans back and looks carefully at Scott. "That's not like you," he says, slowly.

"I know," agrees Scott. "But it felt good. At the time I didn't really know why I was doing it. But as I drove away I felt good. I was wondering why I did and it's because, for those ten seconds when he saw me, I felt better than him. Because I had a fancy car and he didn't."

"That's normal. I get that," admits Sid.

"Yeah but. I've been thinking about how crazy it sounds. I'm getting my kicks out of making other people feel like shit. The more I think about it, the more *crazy* I'm going. Clothes, watches, cars. None of it has any substance. It's a vicious circle. I'm *bored* at work, I've got *nothing* to do."

"Scott, calm down, put this into perspective for a second. Look at us. We..." he corrects himself, *"you* run this company at twenty-four years old, that's...man, that's a big thing."

"Yeah but it's not enough."

"What? What you trying to say?"

"I'm fucking coasting along. I feel like I'm closing a part of me down. This is not what I was meant to do. I'm not here for this! I want to make my..."

"Movie," snaps Sid. "Scott, for fuck's sake. Honestly. Life is just one big movie to you, isn't it. All you wanna do is edit out all the bad bits, the boring bits. You can't just do that, it's not how it works. That is life. It can be boring and repetitive at times and you have to go with it." He speaks more quietly. "You know what, Scott, you're great, I love you but sometimes I just can't stand the way you think."

"Hey, you know, we created a monster here that needs feeding. If I was nineteen again, I would make a different decision. A decision we made years ago is keeping us here now. If we had none of this, none..." He gestures wildly around the room before staring at Sid. "Would you start up this company again tomorrow?"

Sid opens his mouth to speak. Outside, the trees are creaking, their branches scraping against the side of the building, snapping like cracked knuckles.

"No, you wouldn't." Scott answers on Sid's behalf. "Well I have a decision to make and that decision is I'm leaving. And you can come with me or you don't have to but I am not staying here."

"What? Have you gone mad? Are you insane?" Sid clasps his hands behind his back, so that Scott won't see that they are shaking.

"Sid, this is not who we are, we've never been this. I can't be afraid of what's next and I can't just stay here because it's comfortable and nice. That's not who I am and that's not who you are, who we are."

"Dreamchasers," spits Sid. "Yeah, I know. You know what, Scott.

Grow up. You need to grow up. The Dreamchasers thing…"

Scott laughs out loud.

"Don't laugh at me." Sid scrapes back his chair, stands up to face him. "Don't you dare fucking laugh at me, Scott."

"One Dreamchaser, walking out the door!" Scott yells.

"I can't deal with you when you get like this, Scott."

"Auf-fucking-Wiedersehen!" The door slams behind him.

The window is about to cave in. Sid sits down hard on his chair, his pupils diminished to pinpricks. His hands won't still. He swipes hard against the top of his desk, sending the files to the floor. His thoughts dance around the room like the empty carrier bag in 'American Beauty'. *Walk out.* It's always that easy with Scott. Stir everything up and still come out the good guy. Sid takes a deep breath. He can't just leave. Life isn't a game. Surely there comes a time when you have to stop rolling the dice and just slow the fuck down.

The storm makes the walk across the car park a battle of egos. Scott throws his satchel onto the back seat of his convertible. He's made up his mind. He can't go home tonight. He thinks about driving down south, getting away from it all for a couple of days, but the roads would be treacherous on a night like this. Scott leans against his car. If he stays long enough, the icy wind will make the decision for him.

Sid's left his coat in the office and his body tightens with the sudden agony of what feels like stab wounds. The wind is whipping the cotton of his shirt, pinning the fabric against his flexed muscles. He screams Scott's name.

Scott moves slowly around the bonnet towards Sid.

The wind ups its game and they both lose their footing. Sid widens his stance, ready to fight.

Scott looks at him disbelievingly. He thought they were above this. This was how other people resolved things. He doesn't want a fight in the street. Not with Sid. It's not how they work.

Sid shakes his head and pushes at Scott. Show me how much you want it, he thinks. How much you're willing to give up. How much I really mean to you. He shoves Scott again.

The sky is sending spears of hail down onto the tarmac. Scott's face is searing. He pushes back, his hands catching hold of Sid's collar and pinning him up against the side of the car.

Sid doesn't want to hurt him. But Scott is acting like a fucking idiot. He hurts and his body hurts and this fucking day had started so well and... shit. Sid lets go of Scott's hood. There is blood. He steps back, confused.

Even above the storm, they can hear each others breathing.

"Let's talk about this tomorrow," says Scott.

Sid throws up his arms in despair. The blood is his. His shirt is torn and he has a deep scratch on his cheek. "There's nothing left to talk about," he says and turns back towards the office, leaving Scott to it.

"Fuck," he says, grabbing the first aid kit from the desk at reception. Sid's clothes drip icy pools as he makes his way slowly to his office. He is soaked to the bone. He steals a glance in the mirror above his desk. He is glad for the horse-shoe shaped scar that is forming on his left cheek. It distinguishes his cheekbones from his absent father's. His face finally looks like his own. He rests his head against the back of his chair, swallows a couple of paracetamol and waits for the room to stop spinning. When he opens his eyes, it is the first thing he sees. The Dreamchasers list, framed on the wall. He clasps his hands behind his head and lets the anger go.

Fear, as always with Sid, takes longer to dissipate.

Scott puts his foot down and doesn't stop until the street lights have ended and the roads are pitch black and deserted. On a clear night he would have parked up, sat on his bonnet and gazed at the stars. But, in weather like this, there is something mesmerising about the equilibrium between man, machine and the relentless gusts that seem to want rid of them both. Scott is happy to have the road to concentrate on. When the sun begins to spark violet streaks across the moors in his rear-view mirror, he turns around and heads back towards home. He has so much he wants to say to Sid. He just needs a few hours to figure out where the hell to begin.

The debris from the previous night's storm has scarred the car park. The bins are still upturned and the roots of the big oak tree have ripped up from the soil. If you knew where to look, you would see the tiny droplets of blood staining the asphalt. Sid's office, though, is unsullied. The only traces of the previous evening are the shirt and trousers just back from the dry-cleaners, and the fact that he has kept an eye on Scott's office door since six this morning.

"Give us a minute," he says, handing the photograph to the design executive, as he spots Scott skulking slowly along the corridor towards the end of the day. Nervous, he ushers Scott into the room.

Scott smiles feebly. "So, I'm..." he begins.

Closing the door swiftly behind him, Sid holds his hands up. He doesn't want to hear it. Scott stops talking, intrigued as Sid begins to speak.

"The Dalai Lama was once asked what surprised him most about humanity," Sid begins. "He replied: man, because he sacrifices his health in order to make money. And then he sacrifices his money in order to recuperate his health. And he's so anxious about the future that he doesn't enjoy the present. The result being that he doesn't live in the present or the future. He lives as if he's never going to die. And then dies having never really lived." Sid pulls a piece of paper from his jacket pocket and lays it on the table.

It's their list, Scott sees. He doesn't even have time to ask questions. In a flourish, Sid pulls out his fountain pen and crosses out "Operation: ELSA FURY", scoring a big circle around their ultimate aim. He folds the paper deftly away, as though it was no big deal.

"So," smiles Sid. "what's next?"

CHAPTER 28

"So, let me get this right." The woman taps her hand on the bar to emphasise each point, her wrist covered in woven bracelets and festival bands that show how much she's packed into her summer. She is looking at Scott with narrowed eyes and disbelief. "You started a business at fifteen," she begins. "Left school with nothing. Put a couple of thugs behind bars." She rolls her eyes. "Built up a media company with no contacts, no experience, nothing. Turned over millions of pounds within three years. Gave it all up. Left behind everyone and everything you knew to travel halfway across the world. And somehow…" she glances at the skinny guy playing the most polite game of pool she's ever seen. "Somehow kept your friendship intact. Have I missed anything?"

Scott can sense her cynicism. "I know what you're thinking," he says. "What about a pension, security, the future."

The woman takes a sip of her Campari and soda, unimpressed. "And what happens when the money runs out?"

Scott is confused. "It doesn't run out," he tries to explain. "I've got this resource." He taps at the side of his head. He speaks quickly. He can see it in her eyes. He's desperate to convince her, make her see that freedom doesn't have to be time-stamped. You don't have to squeeze it into a gap year. "I can always make more money. It's just a question of coming up with the right idea at the right time. What matters is the bigger picture. What matters is what's driving you."

She shakes her head. She admires Scott's optimism, but it is short-sighted. Just because you get lucky once or twice doesn't mean you should stop making contingency plans.

Scott wonders whether to change the subject, to tell her about the seafood risotto that was brought to their table by mistake in Bora Bora, the way he'd dangled his legs in the perfect turquoise sea as he'd tucked in. Best meal of his life, hands down.

"I dunno," she says. "It sounds like a movie or something."

Scott pulls the pool cue from under Sid's elbow, making him miss his shot. "Hear that?" he shouts over the noise of the stereo. "She said our story sounds like a film."

Sid laughs.

"Why's that so funny?" the woman asks.

"That's why we're here," Scott says. He takes a second to look out of the window. It's taken him a year to get used to the expanse of sky that swallows up his fears in a second. He can't believe people are born here, that they get to say they're from Paradise. That their first views are of lush green vegetation and water so clear you wonder if it's real and he wants to capture it all, struggles to find the right descriptions. Sid is better at that, his camera always close to hand, not needing words. Scott's hands reach for his satchel.

The woman stares at the pile of typed pages Scott has stacked on the bar. "What is it?" she asks.

"This is what a year's solitary confinement with Sid over there does to you."

She assesses the front cover. "*Scott and Sid*," she reads. "What is it, a novel?"

"Film script."

Sid is shaking hands with his pool opponent, pulling up two stools beside Scott. "What you doing?" he says, incredulous that Scott has even brought the script out with them. It should be in the safe back at the apartment, with their passports and their emergency stash of money, where Sid had left it. They'd had a deal. The script was for their eyes only until it was finished. Besides, there is a pint of beer near Scott's elbow and Sid doesn't trust him when he's had a drink.

Scott puts the script away.

"So, what's your plan?" asks Sid's pool opponent, a backpacker from Belgium, wearing a Kiss T-shirt.

"We spend the next year looking for people with money who'll invest in our film."

"How much you talking?"

"One million to start," answers Scott, matter-of-factly.

"Rather you than us," says the Belgian.

Sid senses the pity in his voice. "It's more strategic than it sounds," he says. "It's not just knocking on doors."

The Belgian holds up his hands as if to say, hey, whatever man, I'm not here to argue. "Wanna play?" he asks Scott.

Scott picks up the black ball from the table. "Yeah, why not."

When they are out of earshot, the woman whispers in Sid's ear. "So that was all pure bullshit, right?"

Sid watches Scott make his first move. He has his chin resting on the cue, his steely blue eyes calculating the shot. "Scott's a lot of things," he says, "but bullshitter he is not. It's all true." Sid takes a sip of his juice. "More or less." He leans closer to the woman. "Between you and me, though, I'm not that fussed about leaving. I'd be happy to stay here forever. I can see why they call it Paradise."

Scott watches Sid make his first move. Sid has honed his flirting skills to perfection. Not that they'd needed much work. Before, a kiss at the end of the night had been a bonus. Now it seemed *inevitable* that, at some point in the evening, their table would be graced by a pretty woman or two. Scott isn't interested. He is happy for Sid, though. Their trip gave him the severance he needed, to pack his bags and finally move out of home. Sid had done his time with convention, thinks Scott. Almost a life sentence.

Back at their apartment, Sid is sitting on the balcony, a dictionary on his knee, rifling through the pages of their old notebooks. It's role reversal, Scott realises. Sitting on a sun lounger next to him, Scott feels more at peace than he has in years. In every country visited, he'd booked the biggest apartments they could afford, made sure there was a stash of films waiting for them, a decent restaurant nearby so they didn't have to argue about whose turn it was to cook. He'd been worried that Sid would get bored of him, that he'd do a runner. But it had been exactly what they'd both needed. They are closer than ever.

"I think it's ready," Scott says, looking out across the mountains. There's snow on the caps. If they don't leave soon, it'll be winter.

"It's not perfect," Sid dismisses. "Another month."

"You told me once that I wanted to edit out all the bad parts of life. Put it into a shiny package and sell it to the world. That's never been what this is about. It's not for us anymore."

Sid looks up. Scott is sweeping his hand across the landscape. The lake, the peaks, the sky, nowhere and everywhere.

"It's for *them*," says Scott. "To show *them* it can be done." He adjusts his Ray Bans. "Everyone we meet, everyone we tell our story to. What's their reaction?"

"Complete, utter disbelief." Sid closes the dictionary, remembering the page.

"Cos we prove everything wrong. We up-end the laws of the

universe for them. We're here, not funded by mummy and daddy. We've earned every penny in our accounts. Everyone we've met, they've got the guts to do it. Yeah, to go travelling, to have an adventure for one month, six months, whatever. To do what they want. And then what? Back to normality. You can plot their trajectories five, twenty years ahead!"

"That's a bit harsh, Scott."

"Sid, look. I'm trying to tell you. The script will never be perfect. Life's messy. Our life."

"I guess."

"So, London, yeah?"

Sid carefully packs the script away. "I guess. I mean, yeah. Fuck it, we can't write it forever."

"We're gonna find the money if it kills us." Scott grabs Sid's chin in his hands. "I mean, look at this face! Who wouldn't want to invest in this face?"

Sid breaks free, laughing. "I mean, how hard can it be? Want a beer? I never finished watching 'City of God' with you."

Scott aims the bouncy ball at the fridge, pounding it closed just as Sid opens it. "Better not," he says. "Just booked us flights to London." He flashes Sid a not-at-all-sorry grin. "We leave at seven."

CHAPTER 29

Scott steps inside the lift, glad that it is empty. As the pulleys hiss into motion and the elevator glides upwards, he makes an effort to breathe. Without these small pockets of peace and quiet each day, he'd have caved in years ago. The plated glass lining the elevator fractures his face into Art Deco spikes and he watches his eyes carefully. Tomorrow's meeting is out of his hands. The culmination of everything. He can't help feeling as though, despite everything they've been through together, he never quite has a hold on Sid. It's always been like that. Scott feeling as though he's holding a gun to Sid's head. Sid's problem, thinks Scott, is that he's always waiting for things to fail, so that he can say "I told you so" and return to normality. Sid's reaching his breaking point, Scott can tell. Fifty-three failed opportunities so far, fifty-three potential investors saying no in different ways and it's taking their toll on them. Scott's just waiting for Sid to break.

Scott bounds out of the elevator and into the cold. It's dead up here. He had discovered the untended roof garden on the night they'd moved in. Unable to sleep, he'd wandered the corridors and scaled the steps all the way up to the top. Ventured around the areas not intended for residents' eyes, where air vents are mended with duct tape and the smell of detergent and waste and empty ashtrays are released into the city in tumbling plumes. Eventually, he'd found a fire door with a disabled alarm. He had come up here every night since.

It reassures him, that even the world's most polished facade has a crack in it, that he has managed to find a loose brick amidst the luxury. It is the only place in this city where he can think straight. He pushes open the old fire escape and climbs the steps up onto the roof.

The ground from the twentieth floor is a grid of ruled paper with various axes. People and cars become plot points on a graph, marking their way across town, and the trees swamp green across the page. Skyscrapers that hurt his neck to look at from the ground become architectural masterpieces viewed at eye-level. That realisation from idea to stone: sometimes Scott wishes he had that, a knack for drawing. Not just doodles. He wishes he had a talent like that, something tangible, that would condense all the swirling thoughts in his mind onto paper in black and white. But that would be the easy way out. It's part of the challenge, he thinks. Figuring out how to lead someone through the labyrinth. How to bring them around to his way of thinking.

Scott smirks. He's always been accused of being too cocky, of thinking he is a cut above the rest. And maybe they're right. Because now, looking down at London, Scott wishes he had the guts to jump, because he knows that he is special and he's sure that he would fly. When he wants something badly enough, he makes it happen.

He screams into the sky and watches the starlings flee the scene and run for cover. It's a fine line, he thinks, between ambition and the crazies.

The news breaks for adverts as Sid finishes his workout. The concierge knows to deliver his order fifteen minutes after the wake-up call, but he phones it in just to be sure. By the time he has showered and shaved, his cup of tea is the perfect temperature, waiting for him on the bureau beside the door.

He's not sure what Scott was thinking, booking them into this place. It's a last-ditch attempt, a kick up the arse for both of them. As though, by spending a week living side by side with high-earners, it'll force them to rise to the competition. And then it had happened, a chance meeting in the lobby, a film-loving millionaire on holiday from Monaco. Time on his hands and why not meet. That was three days ago. And now it is judgement day. Do or die, as Scott would say.

Sid slides his silver-linked watch onto his wrist and slaps on some cologne. The bottle, label-less and indistinct, could belong to anyone, could be vinegar, vodka even, but Sid likes to think of it as his signature scent. The simple lines, classic glamour, make him feel streamlined, which is all he ever wants from a day. He remembers the first day he wore it. Before New Zealand, when they were still crossing off dream destinations from their list. An events pitch in L.A. that they were destined to lose. Against the odds, though, they'd won the contract, found themselves being flown in a helicopter over the Mojave Desert. Somewhere between taking off from a rooftop in Palm Springs and puking in the parachute crate, Scott had decided that it was the cologne that made Sid memorable, and he'd kept his friend stocked up with the brand ever since.

Sid's natural expression is a frown. He can't help it. His smile, teeth gleaming to his ears, is always a surprise to people, but it comes more readily these days. Flashing it at himself now, Sid is happy at who he sees. The man grinning back at him is ready to go.

The corridor stretches on, mirrors repeating his dapper image into the distance. Sid tries the lock on the room next door. No luck. He is about to knock when he sees a cleaner approaching. Her make-up is impeccable, long-sleeves barely hiding rockabilly tattoos.

"Hello, hi." He smiles apologetically. "I've left my key inside."

The woman smiles back and unlocks the door. "You British boys..." she says with an American drawl, and Sid's mind flashes to an image of her, framed perfectly on a painted verandah, the Mississippi in the background. It's a hazard of the job these days. They've been spending so long writing the script, Sid's always viewing things through an imaginary lens, adjusting the filters and composition.

"Thank you." He watches her walk down the corridor, then tries the handle.

The door opens an inch. Sid reaches behind it. Without having to think, he squints his eyes, stretches his fingers to full length and knocks the chair away from the door. It tumbles to the ground and the door swings open.

They are both creatures of habit. It has always struck Sid as funny, that Scott should be so afraid of intruders when his own head is full of them.

Sid draws back the curtains, flooding the room in light. Flecks of dust hover in the air. It's as though Scott has been holed up in here for days, all oxygen vacuumed out of the room. Sid is a little disgusted. Scott should be ready by now. The room carries the scattered debris of someone quick to undress. Sid traces the route Scott took last night, picking up clothes from the floor and throwing them into the laundry basket. He rinses away the blonde beard trimmings in the sink and unwraps a new soap from the pyramid of bars beside the taps.

Scott's room is the distorted mirror image of Sid's. Scott sprawls in the middle of the bed. He has taken the cushions from every other chair in the room and they pile high behind his neck. There are a million creases in the bedsheets. Scott's forehead, too, bears evidence of a night spent worrying He takes a long drink from the water bottle. "Where is she?"

"Who?" asks Sid.

"The stunning blonde chick I could hear screaming all night." Scott clambers out of bed. He scratches at the tattoo on his hand.

Sid throws Scott a towel. "She left."

"You must've made an impression."

Sid ignores the swipe. So what if he can never keep them for longer than a week. At least he's getting some. He makes an attempt to straighten out the bed covers. One corner of the duvet up and he tries to fathom where its corresponding cover is. "Sleep well?" he asks Scott.

"Not a wink. Got a good feeling about today, though." Scott rummages around the mini bar, searching for an unused tea bag. The marble counter top is stained from china mugs and covered in crumbs and partly-eaten hotel biscuits. The bin is unused.

As Scott is speaking, Sid walks into the bathroom and turns on the shower. Instantly, the room begins to fog with the heat.

"Hello... Yes, I slept great thanks." Scott holds the hotel phone against his ear and checks his mobile with the other hand. "The guy next to me in room 301 was a little loud last night though!"

Sid glares at Scott. "Ass-hole," he mouths.

Scott whips at Sid with his towel until his friend cracks a smile. "Excellent," he says. "Oh yes, and can I get an Earl Grey tea please... No, no, no milk."

"You getting in the shower or what, then?"

Scott puts his hand over the mouthpiece of the phone. "Sid, you want anything?"

"No thanks, I've had breakfast." Sid finds Scott's suit hanging up in the bathroom. At least he's had it cleaned. That's better than last time.

"Just tea then, that's great, thanks." Scott is a fan of simple interactions that don't require goodbyes. Somebody wants something. Somebody gives something. No need for intimacies. He hangs up the phone and tosses it onto the bed. "I wonder if he shaves his own head or gets it done for him."

Sid checks the time again. "Who?"

"The Dalai Lama."

"Scott. Stop arsing around. Get in the shower. This is the biggest meeting of our lives." Sid arranges Scott's clothes on the bed, picks at a fleck of lint on the suit jacket. He sighs. "Where are your cufflinks?"

"Don't need them." Scott rifles through his papers and finds what he's looking for. The first scene with Olsen. It's been bothering him. There's a detail missing. The writing is illegible to Sid, three blotches with ink-legs cantering across the page. Scott reads it easily, a shortbread biscuit dangling from his mouth. "Did Olsen have a globe in his office?" he shouts to Sid.

"Scott!"

It's a long time since Scott's seen his friend lose his patience. Sid is pointing to the bathroom, his tone of voice like someone failing to train a puppy. Scott snaps the shortbread between his teeth.

"Jesus, Scott, do I need to cancel?" Sid knows he's being a little dramatic, but Scott demands it of him sometimes.

Scott gives Sid a serious look. Sid can be patronising without knowing it. As though this meeting doesn't mean everything to Scott, too. As though there's any danger that he won't be ready in time. That the pair of them won't stride into the meeting, exactly as the clock strikes, each looking impeccable in their own way. He just wants to have all the details right, in his mind, before he gets in there.

Sid carefully hangs up his own suit jacket and sits on the bed.

Something digs into his side and he reaches under the pillow, pulls out a book, recognises it as one he gave Scott that Christmas. Sid lets the pages cascade open, sees the text covered in Scott's writing. He places the book on the table and turns on the radio, loud, to drown out the sound of Scott reciting his film pitch in the shower. Maybe he's taking this seriously after all.

Scott presses the illuminated chrome button again and again. The lift is taking too long.

Sid wears the look effortlessly. At times, he seems to glide. Something about wanting to fit in. With Sid, everything appears seamless. You would never catch Sid itching under his collar, adjusting his watch strap, re-buckling his shoes. He steps into the lift and nods at the businessman already in there. "You need to relax," he tells Scott.

"You know." Scott remembers the writing on his hand, rubs at it until it smudges. "Every so often I feel at ease, as if I'm taking a full breath."

Sid smiles. "Every so often." He catches a glance at the stranger's watch, a fat gold Breitling. Fifteen grand for that, at least. He nudges Scott.

"Hang on," says Scott. "It's ten past seven? Why the hell did you get me up?"

"To see if you were alright."

"What?"

Sid smiles. "I couldn't sleep either."

The door opens at the twelfth floor and the lift is filled with the scent of perfume.

Scott steps aside to let the woman in, then continues, speaking over her head to Sid. "The meeting isn't til nine." He presses the illuminated G button again. "You know I'm not good at waiting..."

The lift door opens and they step out into the lobby. They begin to walk in stride with each other, instinctively, moving more quickly than they need to.

"I think he does," says Sid.

"Does what?"

"Shave his own head."

Scott laughs. The sound bounces back at them from the crystal chandeliers. He pulls Sid's cheek in agreement and nods. Together, they spin through the rotating doors, and the London streets greet them with a cacophony, like old friends. "Let's get a taxi," says Scott. "Drive around for a bit."

"Sure," says Sid. "But we've gotta be there for nine on the dot."

"Black cab though, yeah? Like our first trip here. Let's be old school about this."

"Whatever, sure." Sid smiles. "Scott?"

"Yeah?"

"Today is one of the good days."

Scott adjusts his Ray Bans on the bridge of his nose. He knows what people say. He's been told the sunglasses make him appear arrogant, shifty, make people wonder what he has to hide, but Scott can't hold a meeting without them on. He needs that barrier between him and them, between him and the lights, between him and everything else. He lifts up his glasses and winks at Sid.

The taxi driver lifts his cap and smooths a palm over his hair. He taps his thumbs against the steering wheel and exhales loudly. It's too early in the day for smart arses. "You fucking with me?" he asks his passengers.

Scott and Sid exchange glances in the back seat.

The cabbie weighs up the blonde lad in his rear-view mirror. Twenty-five maybe. Impatient look about him like he's not used to waiting around. The other lad looks normal enough. "You're seriously asking a London cabbie to take you the long way round?"

Scott shrugs, settling himself into the seat, buckling up his seatbelt then thinking better of it. He winds down the window as far as it will go. His fingers drum against his legs. His mind won't settle. "Fancy the scenic route."

"We're really early for a meeting," Sid explains. He passes two fifty-pound notes to the driver. London prices still make him wince but what the hell, anything to keep Scott sitting in one place for a couple of hours. "How's this for starters?"

The cabbie presses the money against his window, glad when the sunlight shows it to be real. He turns to face his passengers. "Mikey," he says, by way of introduction, his face creasing into a smile.

Sid smiles back at him.

As the taxi pulls out into rush hour, Scott focuses on the city, his hands cradling his temples, his lips silently shaping the words of their film synopsis as his mind switches to auto-pilot.

Sid reaches into his pocket for a distraction. He holds his camera in his hands, clicks his way through a thousand photographs. Bali. Australia. Croatia. Hawaii. Their dreams in rectangles. He smiles. Scott somersaulting into a river, Sid emerging victorious a minute later. He keeps clicking. Anything to make the time go faster. He hasn't felt this nervous in years. A life spent learning his lines and it feels like this meeting is what it's all been *for*, all the rehearsals. He imagines the restaurant. White tables. Their entrance. Their one chance to get it right. The perfect pitch.

"You've stopped looking for him," Scott says after a while. He's been watching Sid for fifteen minutes.

"What's that, son?" asks the cabbie.

"Name's Scott. And I was talking to Sid."

Mikey holds up his hands in apology. Hazard of the job, overhearing things. Sometimes they wanna talk, sometimes it's silence the whole damn way.

"Don't mind him, Mikey" says Sid. "He gets like that." He puts down his camera. "Not looking for who?"

"Your dad," says Scott. "First time you're not scanning faces, looking for your dad."

Sid pauses. "It was that obvious?"

"Every city. Thought you were gonna short circuit in New York." Scott laughs. "You were like Johnny 5."

Sid sits back, rests his elbow on the window. He'd always thought he'd been subtle about it. Always had one eye out for his father. Hardly a chance of picking him from a crowd, but Sid couldn't help himself. It had been an instinct, long as he could remember. Like an animal sleeping with one eye open. Who's he kidding, he thinks. Of course Scott had known. Scott had seen right through him since day one.

Mikey makes a left turn towards Regent's Park, immediately regrets it. The traffic is nose to tail. Good job they're not in a rush, he thinks. Usually, at the first sign of a jam, there'd be huffs from the back, exaggerated sighs and frantic phone calls. He eyes up his passengers, wonders what their story is. They're talking now, back and forth, the blonde one animated and the dark-haired lad giving as good as he gets. Arguing about films. There seems a proper connection between them, something unspoken. There's no artifice. None of that silver spoon crap he's used to in the city. Public school brats who can barely make eye contact with skivvies like him. Nah, these lads are different. He likes Scott and Sid already.

Scott looks up, catches Mikey staring. There it is, he thinks.

In these minuscule moments of connection. The whole fucking glorious point of it all. Scott grins. "Wanna hear a story, Mikey?"

"Don't forget to put my name in the credits," says Mikey, stopping the meter and turning to get a proper look at the lads who've just told him their life story. "That's as far as I can take you." He's done his best, got them as close to The Ritz as he can manage. Truth is, he's sorry to be saying goodbye to these two.

"We'll give you a starring role," promises Scott, scrambling to open the taxi door. They're cutting it fine.

"Keep the change, Mikey," Sid says, smiling, tumbling after Scott onto the pavement.

Scott stands on a fire hydrant and scans the surroundings to get his bearings. The Ritz is at the end of this avenue. A thousand obstacles between them and their ultimate aim. They have ten minutes to get there. He looks at Sid. "You know this is it," Scott says. "I can feel it."

"The end?" asks Sid.

Scott grins. "The beginning." He jumps down onto the street, steadies himself against his friend. "You ready?"

Sid gives him a goofy smile like the one Scott remembers from that first day in the classroom. "Born ready," he says, as if there was ever any doubt.

A car backfires and it's like a starting gun, Scott and Sid racing to the finish line, Sid leading the way through the pedestrians, his suit tails gliding behind him as he runs. Apologising to everyone he bumps shoulders with, cars screeching to a halt, dodging women with prams, bewildered glances in return. Scott bounds behind him, knocking his limbs against everything in his path, insults flying his way, kicking out at strangers, pounding on bonnets, unimpressed glares in return. The city is a steeplechase, the intersections looming like too-high hurdles, and Sid grins back at Scott each time they make it. He reaches for Scott's arm and the momentum propels them both forward, laughing like loons. They are flying now. The pavement becomes liquid. They're kicking through the air and then it's a guitar busker and the sound of coins tumbling onto the floor and Sid is shouting sorry and they are laughing even more.

"Two blocks," shouts Sid.

"I'm knackered." Scott stops for a second, panting. Ahead is Piccadilly Circus.

Sid isn't about to give up now. He grabs hold of Scott's shoulders. "See that?" he yells, pointing up at the neon.

Scott looks. The advert stretches up twelves stories of a building. It is impossible to miss.

"That's gonna be our film," declares Sid. He sets off again, unfazed, disappearing into the crowd.

"Shit," says Scott, trying to keep up, laughing harder than he ever has before. He wants it. Chasing through the billboards, Scott sees it all projected up there on the screens. The day he met Sid, the dizziness brought on by Olsen's words, the thrill of London first time round, the crap with his parents, with Sid's mum, the wheeling and dealing, the bust-ups. The dreams that became reality, over and again so that he can barely tell the difference anymore. And for once, he is following Sid. He is pounding the streets of London like every hero or anti-hero he's ever watched up there on the big screen, not stopping for anything, not giving up on that impossible dream until the blood has stopped pumping through his veins.

He catches up with Sid outside The Ritz.

At his usual table inside, someone is ordering a triple espresso, tapping his feet, bored of his world, wanting something good to pour his money into, watching the clock, desperate for an opportunity to dream again.

They stand in front of the glass doors and compose themselves, Scott reflected in one half, Sid in the other. The doors part. Scott fixes Sid with a determined stare. "Let's burn the boats, yeah?"

So, what's next?